The diary of a
social butterfly

By the same author

The End of Innocence

Tender Hooks

The diary of a social butterfly

Moni Mohsin

RANDOM HOUSE INDIA

Published by Random House India in 2009
Twelfth impression in 2014

Copyright © Moni Mohsin 2008

Random House Publishers India Pvt. Ltd.
7th Floor, Infinity Tower C
DLF Cyber City
Gurgaon 122 002, Haryana, India

Random House Group Limited
20 Vauxhall Bridge Road
London SW1V 2SA
United Kingdom

978 81 8400 053 5

Typeset by Line Arts
Printed and bound in India by Replika Press Private Limited

For sale in the Indian Subcontinent only

For Faizi, my very own Kulchoo

Introduction

What? What do you mean, 'who am I'? If you don't know me then all I can say, baba, is that you must be some loser from outer space. *Everyone* knows me. All of Lahore, all of Karachi, all of Isloo—oho, baba, Islamabad—half of Dubai, half of London, all of Khan Market, and all the nice-nice bearers at Imperial Hotel also. But since you seem to be an outer-space-wallah, an astronot, alient or whatever you people are called, chalo, I'll ignore karo your ignorance this one time only, and tell you about me.

I live in Lahore. In a big, fat kothi with a big, fat garden in Gulberg, which is where all the khandani, khaata-peeta types live. And don't listen to the newly-rich cheapsters who live in Defence vaghera and say that, 'No, no, Defence is Lahore's best locality,' because they are liars. They are just jay—jealous, bhai! Honestly, do you know anything? No offence, but you tau seem like a total paindu pastry to me. Anyways, we have ten servants—cook, bearer, two maids (one Filipina and one desi), two drivers (one for me, one for Janoo), sweeper, gardener, and two guards who both carry Kalashnikovs, wear khaki uniforms and play Ludo around the clock at the gate. All of these people look after me, Janoo—uff, bhai, my husband—and our son, Kulchoo.

Kulchoo is thirteen (or is it fourteen?). Anyways, his voice is becoming horse and yesterday I was noticing he needs threading on his upper lips. He likes doing something called Wee and Bookface. Naturally, Kulchoo goes to Aitchison College, which is Lahore's best school for nice rich boys from nice rich families. Janoo also went to Aitchison, and from there only he went to Oxford in London, and from there he came back three years later an Oxen. I shouldn't be saying this, because he is my husband and you are total stranger, but Janoo is very bore. He likes bore things like reading-sheading, watching documentaries and building schools in his stinky old village. Did I tell you Janoo is landed? Well, he is. But unfortunately his lands are not in Gulberg, where everyone could see them and be jay. They are hundred miles away in a bore-sa village called Sharkpur, which I haven't been to, thanks God, for nearly four years.

Janoo's mother is a window, sorry, sorry, I meant widow, and I call her The Old Bag. She is fat, bossy, wears Bata shoes and can't speak English. But thanks God a hundred million times, she doesn't live with us. Janoo has two sisters—the Gruesome Twosome. They are big cheater cocks and always doing competition with me, poor things. Not that anyone can do competition with me. Mummy (that's my mother) says I'm unique.

I am very sophisty, smart and socialist. No ball, no party, no dinner, no coffee morning, no funeral, no GT—uff, now I have to explain GT to you also? Get Together, baba—is complete without me. Naturally, if you are going to be so socialist you also need the right wardrope and the right looks. So I have to get my designer joras and visit my beauty therapists and my jewellers, vaghera, na. Just my selfless little way of supporting Pakistan ki economy. Unlike Janoo, who is a zinda laash, I am very gay. I love travelling—to Dubai, to Singapore, to Harrods—and watching top ki films like *Sex and the City* and *Jab We Met* and reading *Good Times* and *Vogue* and peoples' sections of all the newspapers.

My bagground is not landed, thanks God. We, baba, are Lahoris through and through. I am convent-educated and afterwards I went to Kinnaird College, where all the rich illegible girls go while they are waiting to be snapped up. (Janoo's sisters went to Home Econmics, where all the middle-class or purdah types go.) My family, needless to say, is very sophisty. Daddy worked for a multinationalist company and Mummy was his co-operate wife. Mummy's favourite cousin sister is Aunty Pussy. Her husband, Uncle Kaukab, whom Janoo calls Uncle Cock-Up, was a tax collector. Anyways, they are, mashallah, very well-to-do, with houses here and there, some of which they admit to and some of which they don't. They have one son called Jonkers, who is twice die-vorced, and we are now looking for third wife for him.

My friends are socialists like me. There's Mulloo, Flopsy, Furry and Twinkle. Most of their husbands are bank defaulters but they are all very religious and upright otherwise. Unfortunately my friends are also always doing competition with me. But chalo, I suppose help nahin kar sakteen. After all, it can't be easy knowing me...

The Butterfly
Lahore, 2008

January 2001

Taliban threaten to destroy all statues
Floozie runs off with best friend's husband

Haw, such a big scandal in our group, na! Tonky's wife, Floozie, has run off with his best friend, Boxer, who is married to Floozie's best friend, Dropsy. Just look! What a tamasha. Everybody is talking about it at weddings, darses, parties, everywhere. Floozie's name is mud. Worse than mud. Mud mixed with cow shit, like the pheasants in Janoo's village use to make their houses. (Or do they use straw? Khair, whatever.)

Floozie's name nobody is taking now, except to do gossip of course and to do 'haw, hai', which everyone is doing full time. Mulloo tau has announced to everyone that her doors are closed to Floozie forever till doomday. As Mulloo so rightly points out, if she can do that to her best friend what will she do to her best enemas, sorry, sorry, I mean enemies? Nerves meri shatter ho gayee hain, that is why I am forgetting my English. Vaisay tau I am convent-educated. Even got first prize for reading and obedience in class one. But really, just look at Floozie. She's known Dropsy since KG, when they used to sit next to each other in Little Sweet Hearts School on Jail Road only. Imagine!

What a sleeve ka snake she's turned out to be. Back stabber jaisi na ho tau.

No one is talking about Boxer, though. At least not that much. Because men tau are like this only. Everyone knows. Can't help themselves, na, becharas, poor things. That's why also all the girls, Flopsy, Tinkly, Bobo, Furry, are holding tight to their husbands. Their husbands may be bore, they may be crack, they may be fat, they may be ugly, they may be ancient and decrepid, they may be kanjoos makhi choos even, but it's better than them running off with someone else and the whole world feeling sorry for you. And also wondering what's wrong with you.

But going back to poor Tonky. A crashing bore tau the poor thing's always been, going on and on about price of wheat—they have lands near Sheikhupura only—and his tubewells, and his munshis, and his heart problems—he was triple by-passed only two years ago and since then he'd grown so careful, na, wouldn't even climb stairs, had moved downstairs into guest bedroom leaving Floozie upstairs in case he got breathless and all.

I would've thought that after twenty years of marriage, Floozie must have got used to. But I should've guessed that something was up when she started getting liposeduction done on her bottoms and her chins, and started wearing see-through clothes in winter also. After looking like an ayah for all this time, why would she suddenly change into a champ, I mean vamp, overnight, if not to phasao a man, hain?

Poor old Tonky. He came to our house last night looking like I don't know what. Unshaven, food stains

2

on his shirt, dandruff on his jacket. Bechara, itna Tonky ne feel kiya hai, na, Floozie's running away.

Janoo tried to comfort him in his own sarrhial way. 'The best revenge on a man who runs off with your wife,' he said, 'is to let him keep her.'

Tonky laughed like a hyena but there was a mad gleam in his eye. I think so he's going to have a nervous breakout. I told him to go on Prozac fatta-futt. In fact while he was sitting with us only, I sent the driver to Fazal Din's and told him to bring six packs of it. Tonky took the pills home but now I'm worried keh what if he overdouses? I wonder what happens to you if you take a whole pack of Prozac at once only? Do you die laughing?

But look at Boxer. He's sixty if he's a day. Mummy says when she got married he already had broken voice and stubbly chin, so big he was then. Squirting people with a water pistol and making nuisance of himself. Vaisay he hasn't changed. Still running around with his hair transplant, his leather jacket and tight jeans—so tight that every time he bends down to pick up something, his face turns purple and his eyes look as if they're going to pop out off his head. Must be male menoapplause. Somebody asked him why he'd run off with his friend's wife.

'What to do, yaar? My marriage was empty.'

Humph! As if marriages are thermoses, empty or full. Crack jaisa.

Taubah, baba, this shows you should never trust anyone. Not best friends, not husbands, not anyone. Except your plastic surgeon and your darzi.

3

February 2001

Restoration of assemblies in March likely
Butterfly attends six parties in two days

Hai Allah, I'm so excited na, so excited na, keh bus.
Why? Haw, on which planet are you living? Apollo
thirteen? Don't you know about Basant? Vaisay there
too they must know, I'm hundred per cent sure. How
can they *not* know, when all of Karachi's coming and
all Isloo also? Bet they've got their satter-light dishes
or cable or whatever it is that they have on Apollo
thirteen fixed on all the fun in Lahore. After all,
everybody who is everybody is dissenting on Lahore.
The party groupies like Samir and Muddy and Sana
Hashwani and Abbas Sarfaraz and Tariq Amin and
Choo Choo and Bunty were tau anyways coming, but
now even serious political types as well. I can't name
names just yet, but wait and see on the day and then
tell me if I was wrong.

We've been invited to six parties. First tau there's
the bash at Nevernew Studios; then there's the do on
top floor of Imtiaz Rafi Butt; uske baad there's Royal
Fans walon ka function; and aur pata nahin kya-kya
but finally we'll go to Yusuf Salli's tamasha at the
haveli. Voh tau must hai, na. Particularly this year
because a PTV film crew is coming there only. They

will be doing interviews with family and close friends. Vaisay it would have been so much nicer if it had been BBC, then whole world could've seen my yellow Shamael jora. How women all over the world from China to Chilly would have sarrhoed! Chalo, anyways, we should do Allah ka shukar for PTV. And they, becharas, will also get a break from bore politics.

French polo team is also here these days, na. One of them is really cute. All curly hair and haraami smile and fat-fat muscles. Not that a respectacle married woman like myself would karao him any looks. But you should see the Available Aunties purring in their slinky saris and plunging necklines. Bhai, I tau say, everyone has their izzat in their own hands. Whether you want to look after it like old china or you want to throw it around like a steel degchi is up to you only. Anyways, then there's the big polo ball at Meter Mahal given by Rakshi and Bashir. I think so it's going to be in their garden, all eliminated with fairy lights and diyas and all. Vaisay they could easily have it inside also, so many big-big rooms they've got.

Then Nadia Jamil's getting married. Suna hai lots of celebs are coming. Madhur Jaffery (voh kaun hai?) and somebody else and somebody else. As Janoo says, the roll call of the Good and the Great is about to be taken. I think so he means Basant and parties-sharties. It's getting harder and harder to understand what Janoo means any more. He's started making such elliptic comments. Recently, he's been firing off letters to Mush and Bush about burning of that newspaper, *Frontier Past*. Uff, I said to him, why bother? It's not as if it was your father's paper. Why are you taking it so personally, baba?

March 2001

Kashmiris decline talks with all leaders
Butterfly slaughters sheep

Life's so bore. Basant's also over. Soon Muharram's going to start and then summers will come and everyone will get sealed inside their AC'd rooms and then parties-sharties sub khatam. Bakr Eid came in between, but frankly, yaar, it was so dearie, I mean dreary, that I can't even be bothered to write about it. Janoo wanted to send money to charity, to Edhi Foundation or a hospital or something.

'No need to do bakra,' he said.

'I'm sorry,' I said. 'I may be convent-educated and sophisty and everything, but one thing I won't compromise on—Kulchoo stroking the knife before we do a bakra in our backyard. Stops bad nazar.'

Janoo sighed and said, 'If you insist. But in that case I'll send the money to my mother in the village and she can have the qurbani done there.'

'Never!' I said. 'She'll khao the money and the bakra also.'

'Are you accusing my mother of being a cheap embezzler?' he asked.

'No, ji, an expensive one. A good bakra, if nothing, must be at least ten thou.'

So we had a big fight and now I'm not talking to Janoo. And now he's just come into the room, so I'm going to put away my diary and sit here looking hurt and wounded until he says sorry from the bottoms of his heart for being so sarrhial.

April 2001

Pakistan, Iran agree on broad-based government for
   Afghanistan
Butterfly contemplates career as novelist

Yesterday we did an after dinner drop-in at some
friends. They all started talking about Benazir's
chhutkara and how koi expect nahin kar raha
tha. Janoo said that there's no substitute for a two
party system.

'Haan,' I said, 'Bilkull theek. As long as one party's
in the morning and the other in the evening. Otherwise
one gets very tired showing face at two-two places
in one night.' Hai, sub log itnay impress huay keh
there was complete silence for two minutes full.

I'm so clever I think so I should write a book. What
shall I call it? I know: *My Urban Fraud*. It'll be about
a rich karobari type, import-export wallah, who's
been married thrice, dyes his hair, is sixty five but still
has a thurki gleam in his eye. I fall madly in love with
him and marry him, even though he's beaten all his
wives before and beats me also. I have four or five
children with him while he has affairs with all my
friends, does a huge ghupla, lootos three banks, and
runs away with the maid while I'm left on the ja-
namaaz praying. And then I write my book and tell

everyone about how I had a horrible mother, horrible sister, horrible friends, went to a horrible school, married a horrible man and had a horrible life but still stayed innocent and trusting and religious.

I was still thinking about it when I went to Bapsi's reading at Crow Beaters Gallery in Lahore. Bapsi? Oho, baba, Sidhwa na, writer of *Nice Candy Man* and sister of my favourite Uncle Minnoo of Murree Brewery. Everyone listened so carefully to her reading. Bus, I decided ho na ho, I'm also going to be a writer and give readings to which I will invite everyone except the people who have been horrible to me. Now who would that be?

Well, to start with, my KG teacher who used to make me stand in a corner for calling her 'kameeni'. And the people who came to check me out for rishtas when I was at college but never proposed. Kuttay jaisay. And Mulloo, for not inviting me to her last dinner when she called our whole gang except me. And Flopsy for copying my dining room furniture, and Teensy for stealing my Filipina, and Janoo for calling me a 'talent-free zone'. And of course, Janoo's whole family—The Old Bag, the Gruesome Twosome, and their cheapster husbands and cheapster children for being themselves.

Anyways, to come back to my book, I asked Mummy to give me intro to an old friend of hers who studied at Queen Mary's before it was partitioned. She once wrote a book. Lives in India only. Grey-se hairs, sari, glasses, chappals, bindi. She was here for holidays, visiting her old house on Lawrence Road—it's a school now—and visiting her old school, which I don't know is what now.

10

I asked her what I should write about—'Story-vory, plot-shlot, please koi idea dein na, aunty.'

She peered at me over her bifocals and said, 'Write about something you know.'

Didn't tell Mummy, vaisay, but I minded her comment. Kehti hai, 'Something you know.' Sarrhial jaisi, as if I know nothing. I know so much, so much that if I start telling, half of Lahore will have to flee Pakistan. Who knows Mulloo's real age, hain? Kehti tau hai she's thirty nine only, but my foot thirty nine. She's at least forty five. I know because her waxing-wali told me. She's seen her passport. I don't know how, but she has. And who knows how Furry sneaks out in a Suzuki early in the morning (lest she be recognised in her Merc) and buys her sabzis herself from the mandi only? And pretending never to shop anywhere but Pace and Al-Fatah. Jhoothi. My cook caught her in the mandi red-handed, haggling like a dhoban over the karelas. I also know where and with whom Dubboo, Flopsy's husband, went when he said he was off to do umra to say thank you to Allah for his new flower mill. His travel agent is Mummy's third cousin's niece and she told me he got two business-class tickets to Dubai and made booking in name of Mr and Mrs D Khan at the Humaira Beach Hotel Complex. One room only. Double. With jacuzzi. So don't tell me I don't know anything. Luckily for everyone, I'm too khandani to say...

May 2001

Anti-terrorism law amended in bid to curb sectarianism
The Old Bag has vagina attack

Guess what? The Old Bag has gone and had a heart attack! Last night only, while Janoo and I were sitting in the lounge, eating strawberries and watching *Kaun Banay Ga Crore Patty*, the phone rings and who should it be but one of the Gruesome Twosome, Janoo's younger sister Saika. (I call her 'Psycho'.)

'Ammi chali gayeen,' she wailed like a mad dog howling at the moon. 'Tell Bhaijaan.'

I said, 'Bhaijaan's busy watching *Kaun Banay Ga Crore Patty* and in any case, where's she gone?'

Psycho howled louder and louder until I couldn't hear a word of TV, so I put the phone down and reached for the strawberries.

'Who was that?' Janoo asked.

'Nobody,' I replied. 'Only Psycho.'

'You mean *Saika*,' he said in that sarrhial voice of his. 'What was she saying?'

'Nothing,' I said. 'Only that your Ammi's gone.'

'Gone where?' he asked.

I shrugged. Just then, museebat phone rang again. This time Janoo picked up.

I was lying back on the sofa licking strawberry juice from my fingers when his colour went fak and he started shouting into the phone, 'WHEN? WHERE? HOW?'

Then he banged the phone down, turned to me and announced, 'Ammi's had a heart attack!'

'Must be gas,' I muttered. She's always leaking gas, like an old boiler.

'Get up!' He snapped at me. 'We're leaving for her house right now.'

'At least let me finish *Kaun Banay Ga Crore Patty*,' I protested. 'He's just three questions short of a crore. And the servants will eat all the strawberries if I...'

Janoo didn't even let me finish the sentence. 'Chalo!' he shouted. As if I was his servant or something.

You can imagine the rest. We sped off to The Old Bag's house with him muttering away. 'I'll have to take her to London. I'll fly her out tomorrow. Book her into the Cromwell. I'll call Dr Khalid Hameed. There's got to be a direct flight tomorrow.'

Uss peh tau, my blood really boiled. Here I am begging every summers to go to London, and all The Old Bag has to do is get gas and she's flown out immediately. And probably biz class too. Fat cow.

'What's wrong with Akram Complexed Hospital on Ganda Nala?' I asked. 'She'll feel so at home on Ganda Nala. And anyway, I think so you're gushing to conclusions here. Mind na karna, heart happens only to those who have heart, yani caring types like me. Mummy always said that when food went bad in the fridge I never allowed it to be thrown away, even as a child. I always gave it to the servants and insisted they eat it there and then, so caring I was...'

Anyways, we got to The Old Bag's house and there she was lying on her bed like a collapsed hippo with her eyes shut and muttering, 'Hai, hai.' She was being pressed by the Gruesome Twosome and all her three maids. The minute they saw Janoo they all started bawling like the Sabri brothers and hum nava. The Old Bag immediately sat up and grabbed Janoo's hand and, with tears pouring down her face, started banging on about her 'aakhri lamha' and 'aakhri farmaish'. I couldn't help noticing, however, that respite claiming to have had a heart attack she still hadn't taken off her thirty tola gold karas. They were still jammed on to her fat wrists. I swear, what a tamasha! And so bore also. I tau sat down on the sofa and helped myself to some fruit. Nice shareefas, but not as nice as Mummy's house.

Doctor came and did a check-up and then he asked her about her signs and systems. Apparently The Old Bag had been feeling some tightness in her chest. And breathlessness also. Naturally. If she will wear her shirts so tight what does she expect? All she had to do was to let out some seams and darts in her poplin shirts but no, she had to go and fake a heart attack. Anyways, doctor took Janoo aside while I was having my third shareefa and told him that she'd had a vagina attack. Bas, dekha, I said, it's only vagina, not heart.

'ANGINA!' Janoo shouted.

As if I'm deaf or something. This is the thanks I get for abandoning my TV and my strawberries.

June 2001

Musharraf, Vajpayee urged to agree on N-free zone
Jonkers falls for Miss Shumaila

You know, you can tell about people in one minute flat. Who is khandani and who is not. Now look at Princess Salimah Aga Khan, who visited Lahore a couple of months back. She is real Princess and all, you know, but sooo humble, sooo understated. I met her at a dinner and you know what? She didn't even wear a crown. This is khandani pun.

And then there's Jonkers' new crush: Miss Shumaila, his secretary, ek number ki chaaloo cheez. The way she phussaoed Jonkers is nobody's business. Appearing so naik and shareef from the outside while being a total gold-dogger on the inside. And Jonkers, loser, fool, stuppid, he fell for her book, line and sinker.

He'd call me a thousand times a day and sing her praises—Miss Shumaila this, Miss Shumaila that. I swear my ears had pukkoed. 'She's so respectable, so hard-working, so thrifty, so nice.'

So I tau told him saaf-saaf: 'Jonkers,' I said, 'listen to me. You are son of Pussy Khilafat, grandson of Mr Khilafat, great-grandson of um, um... Mr Khilafat Senior, great-great-grandson of Mr Khilafat Very Senior. How can you marry a nobody?'

'She isn't a nobody,' he protested, his eyes shining dimly like twenty-what kay bulbs behind his inch-thick glasses. 'She is Miss Shumaila and she is also somebody's daughter and somebody else's grand-daughter and great-granddaughter.'

'Oho, baba, she's not somebody's granddaughter, she is nobody's granddaughter.'

'How can you be so snobbish?' he shouted.

'Same way as you can be so stuppid,' I shouted back. 'She is after your money. And the minute she gets it, she'll be off like a bullet from a Kalashnikov. You wait and see. And anyways, if she's so marvellous, why don't you introduce her to your mother? Hain? Why do you keep calling me, expecting me to do your dirty work for you? Persuading Aunty Pussy and all, hain? I'm telling you from now only, someone with a name like Miss Shumaila can only be a gold-dogger.'

'She's not!' Jonkers shouted and slammed the phone.

Ek tau this Jonkers has always been such a problem. So stuppid he is. So bonga. So trusting. Always falling for the wrong types with tight-tight shirts and lose-lose morals. There was that Aqeela, the hairdresser—actually hairdresser bhi nahin, blow-dryer—whom Aunty Pussy paid two lakhs to and peechha chhuraoed. Mummy and I used to call her Akela, the lone wolf. Then there was Typhoon, the telephone receptionist who said 'foon' instead of phone, and wore too much powder and too little deodorant. I was sure Aunty Pussy would cut Miss Shumaila's card in no time, so I wasn't very bothered. After all, Aunty Pussy isn't known as 'Pussy the Past Mistress' for nothing.

The next day while I was still in bed, phone rang. It was Aunty Pussy screaming herself historical. 'That fool! That bloody damn fool!' she shrieked. 'He's gone off to a mosque and got a nikah done to a *secretary*. A *secretary*! And he had the gall to bring that bold little number to the house and introduce her to me as his wife. *His wife!* I was so shocked, I dropped my teacup. Thank *God* it wasn't my Rosenthal.'

'Miss Shumaila?' I breathed.

'You *know* her? You knew about her? You *knew* that he was planning to run off and you never breathed a word?'

'He never said he was going to run off, Aunty Pussy. Just that he had a crush. I thought it would pass, like malaria, you know. I tau even refused to meet her, you know. I could tell from her name only what she would be like. Is she like that?'

'Worse!' wailed Aunty Pussy. 'Much, much worse. She calls toast "toash" and eats her omelette with a teaspoon! What shall I do-hoo-hoo?'

'You should change your locker at the bank and hide the key. And you should take Jonkers' name off your house and put it in your own again. And you should pack away your good shawls and your silver. And then, you should pray.'

God help Aunty Pussy.

July 2001

Democracy road map satisfies Commonwealth
Butterfly purchases jamawar shawl

I tell you, these shawl-wallahs, they're the limit also. Last week this paan-and-surma type came with his bundle on the back of his motorbike. Wanted to sell me a shawl, a jamawar. Big-big paisleys with orange border. Asked for two lakhs. Said it was Nayaab.

'Who's Nayaab?' I asked.

'The shawl, Begum Sahiba,' he replied. 'The shawl is nayaab, you know, unique, one of a kind.'

Now, I'm fine with shahtooshes and things. In fact, I have four—one beige, one green, one brown and one navy blue-and-grey rewindable. Sorry, sorry, I mean reversible. But jamawars are just so bulky, na, keh figure-shigure sub chhup jaata hai. I feel as if I'm wearing a duvet. So I was about to send the shawl-wallah off when I remembered that all my coffee crowd have jamawars. Mulloo, even.

'How much?' I asked.

'Three lakhs,' he said. 'It's over a hundred years old. Unteek hai, Begum Sahiba. Unteek.'

'Antique-shantique koi nahin,' I said. 'One lakh. Not another paisa.'

'One lakh 75.'

'120.'

'170.'

We argued for an hour but he wouldn't budge. So dheet, I tell you, these people are. And so greedy also. Fight over every paisa and every anna. Then I thought, forget it. In any case summers are here and I won't get to wear this shawl for another seven months at least, so why should I let him eat my head for nothing?

'Bas,' I said. 'I've decided. You give me the shawl for 120 and that's final.'

So he said: 'Let's not argue about money. Why don't you keep the shawl overnight and think about it?'

He'd just left when Mulloo called. 'Hai, I'm so excited,' she said.

'Why?' I asked.

'I've fallen in love with this shawl, a really old antique jamawar with huge paisleys and this lovely tangerine-coloured border. That chor Kashmiri came to show it to me because he knows, na, that I am very tasteful, so immediately I saw it and bus, fell in love. But I can't afford it because I bought diamond tops from Carat jewellers last month and Tony will kill me now if I ask for jamawar also, and I got so depress that I was popping three-three Prozacs but then suddenly I remembered the hideous gold bangles and necklace that I got from Tony's family when we married that I've always hated because they're so paindu, and so today I went to Carat and asked him to put a keemat on it and he said it was a lakh and now I think so I'll call the shawl-wallah tomorrow

19

and buy the shawl, will have to haggle a bit but I'm sure he'll give for one-ten, hai, I'm so excited!'

'But don't you feel like you're wearing a duvet when you put on a jamawar?' I asked.

'Who wears a jamawar, yaar?' said Mulloo. 'You just drape it off one shoulder. So classy it looks. Seema Iftikhar has such a nice collection. All the old-money, khandani types have them like other people have napkins.'

So I put the phone down and immediately called the shawl-wallah and handed him 125. Cash. In crisp thousand rupee kay notes. He counted every note, as if I was some kind of jhoothi cheater or something. What happened to trust, to morals, to rakh rakhao, I ask you?

August 2001

No plans to ban jihadi group: Minister
Butterfly attends grand wedding in solitary style

Just my luck to be married to a buddhi rooh, killed joy. Here I am so gay, so gay keh koi hisaab nahin, and there's Janoo more bore than Pal Gore. Only I can cope up with him. Koi aur hoti, she would've die-vorced him long time ago.

Ab dekho, after all those long garmi months of no action, there was one tabahi shaadi—oho, Kasuris ki, baba. Three week long celebrations, khaana to die for, AC'd marquee, two thousand people, anyone who's everyone, from Farooq Leghari and Asghar Khan to Irum and Amo. From Qazi Hussain Ahmed and Nawabzada Nasrullah to Deepak Perwana and Tariq Amin. Only people missing were Benazir and Nawaz. Hai, I forgot, they're both in exile.

Anyways, instead of being happy keh he'd been invited to itni socialist wedding, sorry, I mean socialite wedding, Janoo refused to go. Crack. Said he liked the Kasuris very much but found weddings boring. He said, suno zara, that he'd go after the wedding and wish them in peace and quiet.

'But they haven't invited you to wish them in peace and quiet, they've invited you to a wedding,' I explained in that slow voice doctors use for cracks on TV. 'Kal ko our child will be getting married and what will happen if everyone turns up after the shaadi to wish us? Haan? I'll tell you what will happen. Our shamiana will be empty, our drive will have owls hooting, our food will lie uneaten and will have to be distributed at Data Sahib among the starving, and poor old Kulchoo will receive not a single lifafa and there'll be no raunaq and no halla-gulla and no society photos and no video-wallahs. No one will compare notes on what a tabahi wedding it was. No one will copy the bride's jora. No one will goss about the over-clothes the susraal wore. No one will ooh and aah over the jewellery I wore, and no one will come and say, "Bhai, only you could have done such a zabardast wedding." You know what will happen at Kulchoo's wedding? Nothing. Because no one will come. Our noses will be cut and our faces will be blackened. That's what will happen.'

'Ah,' said Janoo, putting down his papers, 'that would be most unfortunate. Most unfortunate indeed! Twenty years hence, Kulchoo will have a small, unremarkable wedding because of my regrettable lack of social skills. But fear not, my dear. I may be a social disaster but luckily you have yourself to rely on. The indefatigable socialite who hasn't missed a single function of a single wedding in the 15 years that we've been married. Thanks to your heroic efforts we can count on at least 5000 people turning up at our son's wedding. So, really, there's no fear of having to feed the homeless at Data Sahib.'

At that I decided, bus, I damn care. Let him be a loser if he wants, I'm tau going. So I put on my 55,000 ka jora, latkaoed Mummy's ruby jhumkas with matching satlara and solitary ring, and off I went.

First person I bumped into was Pooky, Janoo's cousin sister, who'd tucked the sides of her hijab behind her ears to show off her massive emerald earrings. So cheap she looked. So obvious. She stared pointedly at my diamond solitary ring, which I was wearing on my right hand, and said, 'Isn't that the wrong finger?'

'Isn't Janoo the wrong man?' I replied. Why should I chup raho? She gave me a sarrhial-si look and pounced off.

But I also didn't let her sarrhial comments spoil my fun. I went up to everyone and said at least eight hundred hellos. I know because I kept count. I have an electronic tasbeeh, na, and every time I said hello, I'd click. Later I checked, it was eight hundred and four. Some of them, for instant Asma Jehangir—the guests to whom I said hello, baba—I hadn't seen for months. And others I hadn't seen ever. Frankly, the ones I didn't know looked a little startled, but I smiled brightly and said how nice they looked and how nice it was to see them and accha, ab main chalti hoon because I must ghullo-millo. I wonder if they thought I was crack? Never mind. Let them think whatever they want. After all, I'm not doing it for myself but for Kulchoo.

September 2001

Al Qaeda attacks New York and blows up the Twin Towers
Butterfly loses her patience with Janoo for hogging the TV

Pehlay tau chalo I've been doing guzara with Janoo, but if ever there was a time to get a die-vorce, it's now. I swear, he spends his whole life in front of BBC and CNN, sometimes only he'll switch to Star News. And kambakht, our cable is also fixed so that on channel 53 CNN hai, on 54 Star News and on 55 BBC hai. Ek news khatam hoti hai, tau doosri starts. Majaal hai that Kulchoo and me can switch to sensible channels like MTV or B4U or AXN. Bus, Janoo's hooked on to this America versus Afghanistan drama. I said to Janoo, What's so interesting now? Twin Towers have gone, Pantagone has gone, please switch to B4U. He gives me dirty looks and sticks to bore BBC.

Yesterday, I tau let him have it. 'If anyone should be upset, it should be me. After all, Aunty Pussy, Mummy and me were planning a trip to New York and Mummy's third cousin was coming to Pakistan, leaving her apartment and cat for us to look after for two whole weeks. Mummy'd said keh Pussy'll look after the cat because she herself is quite catty. And then this planes-shlanes thing happened. Worst timing. Kya tha if they'd waited for another two weeks? Main ho hi aati New York.'

Mummy says Masood only's done it—bhai, Twin Towers, what else? Apparently, Masood is the Israeli intelligent agency that does lots of bad things all over the world.

'Why's it called Masood?' I asked Mummy.

She said, 'You don't know, beta, these Jews, they're very clever. They've given it a Muslim name jaan keh so that hamara naam badnaam ho.'

Look at them, I swear! Mummy says on that day, all four thousand Israelis who worked in World Trade Centre were told not to come to work. Masood warned them from before only.

And then some people are saying that Bush had the planes flown into the Twin Towers himself only. Why? Haw, because he wanted an excuse to evade Afghanistan and then Iraq and then Iran and then Syria and then Sudan and then maybe Saudi also. He wants their oil, na. So bhooka he is.

But Aunty Pussy, as usual, doesn't agree. She's always liked to be different, from the time when she was a little girl and wore only ghararas and ate only bhindis. Anyways, she says Pal Gore's done it. Bush rigged the election and now Pal Gore's gone and done this so that Bush's government will fall. And everyone will say, look how incontinent he is! And look at the Indians. They're so jealous, just because we're best friends with America again. Reminds me of Basheeraan who lives in a shack in the slumps across the canal and used to do my waxing. When I chucked her out and hired her neighbour Hameedaan, she became so vicious keh poocho hi na. Just because we've got the Americans ki naukri, Indians are doing all sorts of proper-gainda on their TV.

But Americans also I don't understand. Sometimes they are saying that we Muslims did it because we are jealous of them. Because they live in skyscrappers and condoms and eat Big Macks and hot dogs and watch Jerry Sponger and Opera Winfrey. And they have freedom and we don't.

But darling, who wants to live in a condom, even if it's on a beach in LA, if you have to do your own laundry and cook your own food and wash your own car and even bharao your petrol yourself? I mean, yeh koi life hai? Honestly! I'd much rather live in my kothi in Gulberg with my cook, driver, maid, dhobi, bearer, gardener and chowkidar than any old condom in LA. And as for skyscrappers, taubah baba, what if electricity goes? Who will come up and down those fifty floors, hain? And anyways, I tau love my lawn. So nice for parties in winters. And then nice thing about Gulberg is everyone lives here. Mummy's just round the corner, Flopsy's on my backside, Mulloo's down the road. And because we are so close to the ground, no plane can fly into us...

October 2001

**Pakistan becomes an ally in the US war against terror
Butterfly quashes her sister-in-law's attempts to rise
above herself**

I am so depress. Why? Try living with my in-laws. I
tell you, one day with them and you'd become suicidal.
Kal Janoo's younger sister dropped in. There I was
having a perfectly nice morning, getting my legs
massaged, when suddenly I looked up and there
was Psycho standing in her polyester jora (I wish
someone would tell her that polyester is so over,
yaar!), clutching a box of sweets.

'These gulab jamans are for you, Bhabi,' she said.

'I don't touch mithai,' I said, waving it away.
'Too much of sugar, too much of ghee, too much
of chloroform.'

'You mean cholesterol,' she smiled. 'And never mind,
Bhabi, after the way you slog at the gym to shift those
few stubborn tons you can afford a little indulgence.'

Bitch. How dare she correct my Kinnaird College
English when she only went to a bechara college like
Home Econmics and that too on sifarish? And how
dare she talk about my few extra ounces when she
herself looks like Marilyn Brando in his last years?

'It's just that I haven't seen one of these boxes for so long,' I purred. 'Mithai is so last millennium. But maybe it's still trendy in Iqbal Town—or was it Bahaar Town? That's where your cosy little cottage is, na?'

'My double-storey kothi is in Defence, actually,' she replied. 'Bilal's just got a new job. Very big it is,' she consisted, I mean persisted, boasting like the cheapster that she is. 'He now has two hundred people under him.'

'Must be mowing the grass in the graveyard, then,' I said, yawning delicately.

'And Bilal's sister's been elected to the National Assembly, na,' she continued, ignoring my comment. 'We're all going to Isloo in our new Prado for the swearing-at ceremony.' As if I don't know.

'The same sister who is four feet tall and hunchbacked? Or is it the one who is cross-eyed with buck teeth? Khair, who cares about the election anyway? If I wanted I could win two-two seats tomorrow,' I said.

'Really, Bhabi?' she forced out a laugh, 'and what would be your constituency?'

'Don't you lecture me, ji!' I snapped. 'I have a bigger constitution than you can even dream of, where I prop up the entire economy with thousands of people dependent on my goodwill.'

'And where's that?' she pretended to smile sweetly.

'Liberty Market, of course,' I replied equally sweetly. 'All of Al Fatah, Kitchen Cuisine, Saleem Fabrics, dry fruit-wallah, Ehsan Chappals, even Book Gallery where I buy my *Vogue* and *Harper's*, they

28

would all die if it were not for me! I would only have to nod at them and they'd come pouring out in their thousands giving me ten-ten votes each.'

Thanks God after that she stormed out, leaving me with my maalish woman. I threw the mithai to Kulchoo's labradog but afterwards I watched him carefully to see whether he died a slow horrible death. You never know with these jealous in-laws...

November 2001

NATO forces invade Afghanistan
Butterfly wonders why the invasion should dictate her social life

Janoo's given me ultimatum. He says he's not going to any parties or any balls or any shaadis this winters.

'Bhai, why?' I asked.

'Because I don't feel like it,' he said.

'And why you don't feel like?'

'I'm just not in the mood. That's all.'

'And why you are not in mood?'

'I'm not in the mood because of the war in Afghanistan. I don't have it in me to party at present.'

'But you were being so happy that Talibans were being beaten. You tau were clapping and shouting and saying they were running like rabbits. Now you've changed your mind. Become a hypocrite? Hain?'

'No, I haven't become a hypocrite,' he said with gritted teeth. 'I'm still delighted that the Taliban are being ousted, but I don't like to see Afghanistan being bombed yet again.'

'So they should have thought of that, na, before inviting Osama to be their house guest, nahin?'

'I don't think ordinary Afghans had any say in that.'

'But ordinary Afghans can have say in whether we go to parties or not?'

'Oh, for God's sake!' shouted Janoo. 'I don't know why I even bother talking to you.'

'Because you are so bore that no one else wants to listen to you!' I shouted back. 'And I also only listen because I'm forced to.'

So Janoo took a deep breath and said quietly, 'I don't want to party while Rome burns.'

Rome? Are they bombing Rome? Has Osama run there now? Haw. No one even told me. Now I suppose Janoo won't want to go out because of Italians. Mujhay tau lagta hai he is finding bahaanas. The more I think, the more I think so keh maybe he doesn't like parties.

31

December 2001

Mullah Omar flees Kabul
Why, asks Butterfly, did he not go to the mountains and
  become a 'gorilla'?

Yeh Mullah Omar nay kya bongi mari hai, yaar? How
he was leader of Taliban if he was such a darpoke,
hain? Chalo, okay, you can't stand so much of
bombing but at least you can go into the mountains
and become a gorilla like Osama. Instead, he's sneaked
off on a motorbike from the middle of a bazaar. And
look at the Americans, also! Standing around in the
bazaar scratching their heads while he escapes from
under their noses in broad daylight. And that also on
a scooter! Such losers! And everyone keeps saying
they are so chalaak, so chalaak they have satter-lights
that can read the lines on your palms and tell your
future from outer space. Humph! As far as I can tell,
baba, they can't even read the number plate of Mullah
Omar's scooter. Main tau honestly bohat disappoint
hui hoon.

Vaisay, really, Mullah Omar's also blackened our
faces in front of the whole world. Uss say be worst,
he's blackened my face in front of Janoo. I was so
sure, na, that Mullah Omar would fight till death like
Muscle Crowe in *The Gladiator* that I even made a

bet with Janoo, who predicated that the Taliban would scatter like ashes in the wind. I said, some people have more guts than to bhaago, ji. And now look what's happened. I'm feeling so angry, na. So let down. The least they could have done was to think about my bet before shaving their beards and scurrying off like clean-shaven rats.

On top, Janoo keeps rubbing it in. 'So, where's your precious Mullah Omar now?' he asks, grinning from year to year.

Uff, at times like these, I just can't take him. So irritating he is. Charroes on my nerves so much. First tau I kept listening quietly. But then I also sunaoed him. 'When I married you,' I said, 'I thought I'd found Mr Right. I would have thought a hundred-hundred times before saying yes to the maulvi, if I'd known your first name was "Always".'

January 2002

Powell to discuss Indian demands with Musharraf
Butterfly demands Janoo be more socialist

I wish the year was full of Decembers and Januarys and Februarys. No more bore Junes, Julys and Augusts, when nothing happens. Bas, all-year parties-sharties, balls-volls, weddings-sheddings, return of all the abroad-wallahs, constant aana-jaana, new joras, afra tafri—hai, how nice that would be, na. This year tau the winters have been totally aafat.

First there was the Sindh Club Ball at Sindh Club only. What a tabahi do, yaar. Fifteen hundred people and voh bhi aik say aik best. Hussain—oho, Haroon, baba—Abbas Sarfaraz, Salman and Sally, Irum and Irshad, Furry and Fussy, hai, and my best friend Topsy and her sister Turvy. And Gulgee, Sherry and Nadeem and the Rehmatullahs—yani anyone who's everyone was there. Main nay itna enjoy kiya dancing all those Indian ke Bollywood numbers keh poocho hi na. I think so the only person who didn't enjoy was buddhi rooh Janoo, but then what's new?

All evening he sat frowning moodily into his glass. I asked keh what's your problem, baba? He said, 'Here we are on the verge of war with India, and everyone's dancing away as if it was a bright new dawn,' and he drained his glass in one gulp.

Frankly speaking, I really don't know what to do with Janoo now. Maybe I should send him to a shrimp. But I shouldn't say anything in front of him, kyoon keh mind na kar jaye. Even though he's a buddhi rooh, sarrhi boti, I still have to keep on the bright side of him because the Lady Duffer Ball is still to come and I have to drag him to it. As it is, getting him to go to the Sindh Club Ball was like getting Vajpayee to go on a picnic with Musharraf. Uff, he's become such a stuttering block in the path of my social life, na. Janoo, not Vajpayee. Anyways, chhoro Janoo ko. Why waste time talking about that loser when I could be telling you about this tabahi party in Lahore that I went to?

Organised by Jalal—Salahuddin, na—at Isbah's house only. Three hundred people in, and five hundred out on the waiting list, shivering in the foggy cold. Felt so good walking past all those shivering hopefuls with my nose in the hair. Uff, inside it was even more amazing, with all those thin-thin models in their little-little clothes and high-high heels. And all the silver-haired uncles lounging around on sofas watching them dance from under lowered lids. And the blonde aunties watching their uncle-husbands like Batman watches the Joker. Bar flowing bar-bar. And platters of sushi going past. I tried a sushi nivaala but it tasted all kacha-kacha. I think so they'd forgotten to cook it. So when nobody was looking I quickly spat it out into a bush, wiped my mouth, reapplied my lipstick—MAC ki Russian Red—and teetered off to the dance floor on my six-inch heels. So much action, yaar. I wish January would last the whole year. Without the fog, but.

February 2002

Daniel Pearl abducted and executed in Karachi
Butterfly prepares for Basant

'I think so my best month is February,' I told Janoo as we were driving to Twinkle and Bobo's for dinner. 'I used to think ke December is my best, but February uss se bhi best hai.'

'I agree. There's something uplifting about spring,' he said.

'Particularly the springs of a Merc, they tau are the most uplifting,' I said, wondering how we'd got on to topic of car suspenses. Sometimes I think Janoo's metre has turned. 'Pajero is also okay, but I think so maybe Prado is better.'

'I meant spring, as in season. You know, blossoms and flowers and birds and balmy weather?' sighed Janoo.

So that's why he was talking of springs. He's not totally crack, thanks God.

'Spring-shing koh maro goli,' I replied. 'I was talking of Basant. Uff, I can't wait. The whole week is going to be wall-to-wall functions. I'll be going to so many parties that I won't even have time to say hello to anyone.'

Janoo gave me a funny-si look, but just at that moment we arrived at Twinkle and Bobo's so I didn't have to ask keh bhai, why you are giving me such funny-funny looks?

Dinner wasn't too bad. Small-sa tha. About thirty people only. Half inside, half outside. Some sitting in sitting room, some lounging in lounge, some, as Janoo said, inhaling grass on the grass. I think so he meant the scents of springs and the smell of new grass, vaghera. Food was from Avari, although Twinkle pretended her cook had done it. Jhoothi. I've ordered those fat-fat, fried-fried prawns myself so many times. And not to mention the cold slaw and the smoked salman and the black forest chatto and the chocolate mouse. Sub from there only. Honestly, I don't know why people have to lie, particularly when they know they're going to be found out. Also pretended she'd done the flowers herself, when I know she'd stolen the arrangements from the Gurgling Fridges-walon ka function yesterday. I saw her with my own eyes only, sneaking off with the centre ki arrangement hidden under her fake pashmina shawl when she thought no one was looking. Uff, taubah! So much of lies. So much of reception.

Anyways, talk was all about the coming parties. Janoo says a lot of the Basant parties will be Coke-fuelled. Voh sponsor kar rahe hain, na. They and Emirates. Allah unko khush rakhe for making so many deserving people happy. Also, Razzak Dawood's son is tying the string. The wedding will be in Karachi and Lahore over a whole week. We're sure to get invited because Janoo knows him from before. Must remind Janoo to call him and just do hello-hi to refresh his memories. And phir Imran is having a fundraiser with Amitabh in his hospital. I wish vaisay he'd asked Shahrukh Khan. Amitabh is also not bad, but ab zara aged ho gya hai. Bechara.

March 2002

Al Qaeda casualties not known: US
Uncle Pansy passes away without revealing Swiss bank account number

Mummy telephoned early this morning, about twelve-ish, while I was still in bed, to tell me that Uncle Pansy had gone.

'Gone where?' I yawned.

'To Him.'

'To whom?'

'*Him.*'

'Who's he?'

'Oho, baba, God. Him. Allah Mian.'

'Oh *Him*,' I said. 'Why didn't you say so?'

'I did say so.'

'No, you didn't.'

'I did.'

'Didn't.'

'*Did!*' She shouted. 'For God's sake, stop arguing.'

I was about to slam the phone down when I realised what she had said. 'You mean he's dead?' I asked.

'Yes.'

'Haw, hai,' I said. 'How? When?'

'Last night in his sleep.'

'Poor thing! So that means he didn't find out until the morning, when he tried to wake up but couldn't.'

'Something like that.'

'But chalo,' I said to Mummy. 'He lived to a respectful age, thrice married, seven children, two grandchildren, lived a very full-up life. I think so he must've been seventy seven at least. When was his birthday?'

'July 15th,' she said.

'Which year?' I asked.

'Every year,' she said.

'No, Mummy. I mean, when was Uncle Pansy's birthday?'

Again she said, 'July 15th.'

'But which *year*, Mummy?'

'I've *told* you, na, every year,' she said. 'Except next year.'

Poor Mummy, she's become sterile. Everything she forgets.

Anyways, now we have to do the funeral and burial, because Uncle Pansy'd fought with his last wife and all his children. Not that he's left anything to us. Shouldn't say bad things about deer departeds but such a kanjoos makhi choos he was. Mummy says everything of Uncle Pansy's is in a numbered account in Swizzerland. His paintings—four-four-five-five Chughtais he had—he'd also put there. He'd even sold his carpets and his silver. No one knows the number of his account because, God bless him, he was so kameena. He didn't even trust Mummy, his real sister, with the number. She says it's probably four-two-zero. I think so it's zero-zero-seven, chalaak as Uncle Pansy was. But honestly, least he could have done was to give Mummy the keys of his locker in Swizzerland so she could pay for his funeral. It's not fair, na, to expect others to pay. Like we'll have to now. Or else everyone will talk.

Anyways, Uncle Pansy, however kameena he may have been in other ways, was quite considerate in some ways. I mean he could've died before the LRBT Ball, but he didn't. Or he could've died during Basant even, but he didn't. Instead he died in Muharram after finish of party/shaadi season and before start of London season. So we didn't have to cancel anything. Thanks God.

But I still wonder where the account is and who knows the number. Someone must be knowing. Maybe I'll get someone to hypnotise Uncle Pansy himself and ask. Oho, forgot. He tau has already gone to Him. I've heard sometimes people give numbers of their birthdays for their accounts and things. What did Mummy say was Uncle Pansy's? Haan, July 15th. So that's 15. And July's six. Or is it seven? Now what's the rest? I think so I better call Mummy and ask.

'Hello? Mummy? You know Uncle Pansy? When was his birthday?'

'July fifteenth.'

'But what year?'

'Every year. How many times do I have to tell you?'

'But when was he *born*? What *year*? Hello, Mummy, are you there? You said once that he was five years older than you. What year were you born?'

There was silence on the other end.

41

'Mummy? Can you hear me? What year were you born? Tell, na, Mummy, because I think so I might be able to find his numbered account that way.'

'I can't hear, darling, line's gone all fuzzy.'

Strange, I thought, I can hear her as clearly as if she was sitting opposite me.

'Mummy,' I shouted. 'WHAT YEAR WERE YOU BORN?'

'Uff, beta, it's hopeless. Can't hear anything at all. I'll have to ring off. Byeeee.'

April 2002

General Musharraf prepares for referendum
Butterfly dismisses her sweepress

Ek tau main itni fed up ho gayee hoon, na, of servants and their crooked taur tareekas. So much of lies they tell, and so much of bakwaas they do. Constantly trying to pull the wool over our flies.

Now look at my sweepress. On Monday she maaroed another chutti. When she rolled in on Tuesday, bold as Brasso, I asked, 'Why you didn't come yesterday, haan?'

'Because Musharrat had borrowed for himself the minibus I take from Dharampura to Gulberg,' she replied.

'Why would Musharraf need your minibus?' I shouted. 'Doesn't he have a hundred-hundred Mercs to ride in?'

'For his rally in Minar-e-Pakistan,' she whimpered. 'All the buses, minibuses and even the traalas they took for Musharrat's rally.' (Aik tau these illiterates keep calling him Musharrat instead of Musharraf. I think so they confuse him with Musarrat, as in Musarrat Shaheen the actress.)

'Who took?' But before she could answer, I shouted, 'Sub jhooth! I'm going to throw you out because you are a liar. *And* you came late.'

'But Bibi,' she wailed, 'I'm not lying. I swear on my dead mother's head.'

Uff, aik tau they do so much of drama also.

'The same mother who died three times last year, and for whose every death you took ten-ten days off? That mother?' I asked.

But just imagine, the cheeks! Now I know for a fact that Musharraf came to Lahore by helicopter, which landed on the Minar itself. It said so in the news, even. Which damn fool crack would take a sweepress' minibus when he had a helicopter at his disposable?

So I told her very quietly that I was deeply disappointed in her attempts to befool me and the one thing, the *only* thing (apart from Janoo's family, of course), that I wouldn't tolerate was liars and schemers. And she should be ashamed of herself after everything I had done for her, giving her ten days off every time her mother died and not even cutting her days off from her celery as Fluffy or Mulloo would have, and not even deducing the cost of the cut-glass vase that she broke last month, which my sister-in-law had given to me. (Actually, I'd always hated that hideous thing that Janoo's horrid sister, Cobra—okay baba, Kubra—had brought for me from Jeddah and was sooo reliefed when it finally broke, but of course I wasn't about to tell the sweepress.) So I said to her that I was a good, kind-hearted sole, whose only fault was that she was too good and kind-hearted and so everybody takes my advantage, but I have my limits also—and Janoo always says I'm very limited—and bus, enough is enough, aur bohat ho gayee, and with that I kicked her out. One has to take a stand with these people, na, otherwise they take walks all over one.

When I tried to tell Janoo about it next morning, he completely ignore karoed me, so busy he was with his new newspaper, *The Daily Times*. Honestly, he read the paper like it was a Jackie Collins novel, from cover to cover. But I myself didn't like it. No fashion, no gossip, only news about bore-bore countries like Middle East and bore-bore things about Musharraf's Preferendum.

Anyways, when finally Janoo put down the paper, I told him about my principaled stand with the sweepress.

'She was probably telling the truth. Didn't you know that Musharraf's toady district councillors had confiscated all public transport for the day? So they could bus in their constituents to Musharraf's historic rally? You should read the papers sometimes,' he said disgustedly.

It was on the trip of my tongue to say keh, 'Fox dekh-dekh keh behosh ho gayeen hoon,' but there was no mention, no nothing of Preferendum and minbuses in it, and then I thought, forget it. It will only lead to a tu-tu-main-main.

Next day when I woke up at my usual eleven o'clock and saw the house, I noticed that it was beginning to look dirty with so much of dust everywhere. So I sent a message to the sweepress to say that I'd forgiven her, because I was a good, kind-hearted sole and she could come back. Let's see, now, whether she comes. Aik tau so much of nakhras these people do and so spoilt they are! Honestly!

May 2002

India gives Pakistan two month deadline
Butterfly ponders the essentials of a chic bunker

Hai, hum ne itna enjoy kiya, na, Murree mein. Janoo's Oxbridge society had a GT (oho, baba, how many times I have to tell you, Get Together) at Saigol Lodge in Murree only. Everyone came. Pehlay there was golf, then lunch, and then sub se best, gup-shup. I was sitting there with my sunblock on and my dupatta pulled over my face—in case tan na ho jaoon because mountains pay the sun is very strong—and chatting to Mulloo and Frisky, when I felt my chair shake.

'Hai Allah, earthquake!' I shrieked.

Mulloo, who was applying her lipstick, looked up briefly from her compact.

'Don't worry, even if it is an earthquake, it'll only affect the poor parts of town. Earthquakes are very considerate that way.'

'But what if it's a bomb?' asked Frisky. 'Bobo says war honay wali hai.'

Yeh tau sun keh, I felt my colour go fak. All this time I've been telling Janoo ke chalo, let's go to London early this year. Why do we have to stay here and take all this tension-vension when we could be in Shelfridges enjoying their Bollywood ka Season and meeting Amitabh and drooling over Dimple's bedroom, which Totty told me (who's just come back from London and all), has been flown out pura-ka-pura from Bombay only. Imagine, seeing the bed she sleeps in and the table she sits on to do her make-up! Also, they've got all those designers like Rohit Ball and Shyam Someone. And all the clothes that Hrithik Roshan and Kajol and my favourite shweetoo-sha darling, Shahrukh, wore in their films. But Janoo refuses to go.

'I'm not deserting my country in its hour of need,' he said flatly.

'And what about my hour of need?' I replied. 'My Dr Seebag cream is gone, my YSL Rouge Eclair is finished, my La Perla bras have become dheela—size, Allah ka shukar, is still same but elastic's gone—and my shoes are looking so last year.'

Janoo looked at me as if I'd gone mad. 'Does it not matter to you in the slightest that we may be on the verge of a nuclear war?' he asked.

'Of course it matters,' I yelled back. 'Issi liye tau I'm saying let's go. Why would I want to stay here and become a suttee when I'm not even Hindu?'

'I'll build you a bunker in the back garden,' he said, shaking his head. 'You can sit there and apply your make-up every day, while planes zoom overhead.'

'I'm not going in any bunker which doesn't have AC and generator and cable TV and three-three phone lines and marble bathroom and jacuzzi. And I don't want to be tucked away in the back garden where no one can see me. I want to be in the front, by the rockery.'

June 2002

Osama not here: Musharraf
Cousin Oscar Hake here: Butterfly

So much fun I'm having these days. A nephew of mine is visiting from America, na. His name is Asghar Haq but he's lived so long in Mary's Land in Washington that he calls himself Oscar Hake. His father, Ayub, has big halal meat business there. He's a millionaire I don't know how-how many times and that too in dollars, not stupid rupees. But he wasn't always like that.

When my cousin Minnie got married to Ayub, everybody said, 'Haw, hai, bechari Minnie', because he wasn't from Karachi or Lahore but bore, backward Gujranwala and he had a small-sa meat ka business. Mummy used to call him 'Mayub the butcher'. But what to do, na? Minnie was getting quite aged—at least twenty-nine—and rishtas weren't coming, so her mother married her off so that people wouldn't say, 'Haw, hai, bechari Minnie. Us ka nahin hua, na.'

But then they migrated to America because his lottery came in American Consulate—in the good old days, before the Americans became all mean and kanjoos and stopped giving visas—and there he set up his business. Before we knew it, they'd bought a mention in the suburbs with a swimming pool and land-escaped garden and guest house and servants.

Minnie tau changed overnight. Bechari used to be quite plumpish and quite shortish. And darkish also. Ab tau, she's so thin, spends all her time in the gym and has a personal trainer, and I think so thori si liposeduction bhi karwai hai. Also I think she's had chemical peel done because her colour has become creamy-creamy jaisa. I don't think so it's just Jolen ka kamaal. And she wears killer heels and killer clothes, all designer, and looks tabahi. And of course, Ayub bhai tau is sooo nice, na. He's invited us all to come and stay. Mummy says she's going first, because she's always respected Ayub bhai from the bottoms of her heart.

Khair, I asked Oscar what his mummy is up to these days.

'Mom?' he said, rolling his eyes. 'Aw, she's either playing bridge with some other frustrated housewives or off having her colon irrigated.'

I must tell Janoo to get his crops done the same way. If Minnie's doing it, it must be right.

Anyways, Oscar is sooo funny and sho shweet. Calls himself The Dood. I think so he means dud. Sara waqt apne baaray mein jokes crack karta rehta hai. So self-defecating he is. And so considerate also. Spends hours in his room and when he comes out it smells so, so… sweet and herby and strange. Like the smell Peshawar bazaars have. And he smiles all the time and speaks slow-slow and is a little bit bonga, to tell you the truth, with his uncombed greasy hair and his huge, baggy-si jeans hanging down from his bony hips, as if he'd done potty in them. But I tau haven't said even a word. Baba, mind na kar lay, and then if he tells his father he might take back his invitation.

Janoo says he's just an ABCD loser. ABCD? Haw baba, don't you know? American Born Confused Desi. But Janoo is just jealous because he doesn't have anyone half as rich or half as sophisty as Oscar in his paindu pastry family. So as usual I ignored.

Shweetoo, Oscar's so worried about the bombs-shombs. Innocent jaisa. Just like a foreigner. Vaisay how awful Karachi is, na. Imagine, poor Sindh Club members playing tennis and suddenly having an arm flung in their faces after the American Consulate bombing. Chalo, thanks God, didn't happen during a party on the lawns.

Must rush. I've given a khaana to show off my trendy new nephew to Mulloo, Fluffy, vaghera. Unko bhi pata chaley, in how much water we are.

July 2002

Bangladesh welcomes Musharraf's regret for '71 war
Butterfly regrets her woeful lack of a British visa

Look at Aunty Pussy, honestly. She's managed to get a visa, not only London ka but also a Shagging Visa, which means she can go to France, Spain, Italy, vaghera. And poor Mummy's been refused. What I want to know is how Aunty Pussy's getting it. I think so she's doing something from inside-inside only. On top she pretends to be so innocent jaisi.

'Haw, you all are not going?' she asked me, knowing fully well that poor Mummy's been refused and I'm reapplying next week. 'I thought they were giving visas out like laddoos only,' she said.

Actually, it's all Mummy's fault. Who told her to go and stand in the queue at the embassy with sunblock, sunglasses and head-scarf? Naturally, they thought she was a hijabi fundo and mistooked her for Al Qaeda. Now, who's going to explain to these polaroid gora visa officers that all Mummy was trying to do was avoid a tan?

Vaisay honestly, these stuppids should be given lessons in what's what and who's who in Pakistan before they are posted here. I mean, they should know from just looking at us with our Jimmy Shoe shoes and the two-two-carrot diamond solitary studs in our years and our nice-nice, fair-fair skin that we are nice, rich, khaata-peeta, khandani types who've been to London hundred-hundred times. We are hardly the types who are going to become runaways in London and get jobs in their crash'n carrys and marry cockney goras and become kaala angrezes who live in Councillors keh houses and eat up the state. Nor are we beardo-weirdos who are going to drive planes into their buildings. They don't even know this much, these stuppids.

But obviously, lots of peoples are getting it even apart from Aunty Pussy. Look at Irum and Amo, Yusuf Salahuddin, Salman Taseer, Sheila Saigol, Raunak Lakhani, Abbas Sarfaraz—all going mazzay say to Harrods sale. I've tau even stopped going to Al-Fatah, in fear that I'll be spotted and pitied for being stuck up in Lahore. Last weekend, I sneaked over to Karachi to get all the essentials at Agha's—sunblock, La Prarry products, latest *Vogue*, Hagendaze and Oral ki cookies for Kulchoo. And guess what? Bumped into Zarmeen, who lives in London and is the only person who comes in the opposite direction in the summers.

Before she could say anything, I said, 'Hi, how are you? I'm only here because I'm flying out from Karachi to London, na, rented a flat there, na, right on the back side of Albert's Hall.' Luckily, by then it came her turn at the till and I ran off. Just about managed to get into the car before bumping into anyone else.

Can you imagine how my nose will be cut if I don't get the visa now? I'll never be able to show my face in society. How Mulloo will laugh. How Topsy will

August 2002

Indian Air Force bombs LoC
Butterfly gets a dose of culture

Uff! Itni main exhaust ho gayee hoon, na, after this three-city tour of that small Indian god, Aruna Dhati Roy, which the TFT-wallahs had arranged. Ek tau I don't know why people keep calling her a small god.

I'll never forgive the organisers, but. Kanjoos jaisay, they never sent me a card even. First, I tried pulling stings. Aunty Pussy's best friend's son is a district counsellor, and when he didn't listen, I just called them myself and said: 'Why aren't you giving, ji?

Don't you know who I am?'

Guts dekho, some chaprassi there said, 'Why don't you email in your request like everyone else?'

I felt like replying, 'Because I'm not everyone else.' But then I thought, why do arguing with chaprassi types? So I begged Kulchoo to do an email for me.

'What's the point?' he asked. 'You'll never be ready by 2:30 pm, which is when the event starts.'

Thanks God for Janoo, though. Chalaak jaisa, he had emailed in his request and got his ticket. Luckily, I saw the card when it arrived. I went barging into the study and shouted at him, 'What is this? Akele-akele? I also want!'

'But you have no interest in writing or books or politics or activism,' he said. 'Or anything worthwhile, for that matter.'

'Why, ji? Don't I have interest in society? Don't I have interest in hotels? In events? In going out and about? Anyone who's anyone will be there. Mulloo's going, Topsy's going, even Mummy's got a ticket. If I don't go, all my social cred will go up in smoke. My reputation will be in totters. Mujhe naheen pata, get me a card!'

So anyways, he filled in the email for me, and where they asked for 'profession', he wrote: 'lead actress in soap opera'. Let him do as much bakwaas as he wants. I'm least bothered, as long as I get the card.

Achha hee kiya, because EVERYONE was there. ALL of Lahore. Mummy and Aunty Pussy, Mulloo and Tony, Fluffy and Flopsy, MT and VD, Jonkers, Bobby, Baby, Bobo, Nikki, Sammy, Tammy. Even Janoo's sisters, the Gruesome Twosome, and their hideous husbands had weasled their way in. Vaisay there were lots of people I didn't know also. Wonder who they were and how they managed to get in?

It was nice event but problem was there was too much of talking. Long-long, bore-bore questions and long-long, bore-bore answers and long-long, bore-bore speeches, vaghera. Loved Aruna Dhati's sari, vaisay. Janoo cried when Aruna Dhati finished her speech. So emotionally unstable he is. But thanks God he had the decency to weep silently and not bawl out loud and shame me in front of everyone. Vaisay what there was to cry about, I don't know. It was hardly as if someone had died or something.

Chalo, despite of Janoo letting me down, I did my bit of culture. Now I don't have to do for another three years.

September 2002

US planning war in Iraq
Butterfly planning peace with India

Hai shukar thousand-thousand times summers are going. I tau give shukranay ki niaz every time September comes. Have you seen *Come September*? Such a lovely film with Frock Hudson and Gina Laylosomebody. Old, but nice. And made for Pakistan, only. Honestly, this summer was so bad, so bad, keh main tau bilkull boil ho chuki thi, not to mention bore. GTs are okay but they can't take the place of a tabahi party. Also, Aruna Dhati vaghera's coming for the TFT bash is also all fine, but all said and done, she's a bit serious and a bit bore, nahin? Vaisay between you and me, I tau was quite disappointed with her. I mean Nobel Prize winner (or was it the Bookish Prize? Khair, whatever!) and she wasn't even wearing a designer jora!

Now, look at Danielle Steal. So nice she looks in her soft-focus photos with her big-big diamonds and her high-lit, blow-dried hair. And Barbara Cartland, who was older than Aunty Pussy even, only had her false eyelashes prized off in her coffin. So vain she was. And it's not as if Aruna Dhati is not pretty or something. She could look quite nice with high heels and ironed, streaked hair and some of YSL's Touché Eclair and Landcomb ka mascara and MAC ki lipstick, vaghera. But if she is least bothered, I can't do zabardasti with her. I suppose live and let die. Vaisay such a waste. Haina?

Hai, I hope so we can make friends with India. Imagine hopping across to Delhi every time you need a new outfit, or a new earrings ka set, or even a new party. Imagine being invited to the Tatas and the Godrejs and ringing up Shobha Day for hello-hi whenever I want. Uff, mazzay! Then maybe even Janoo can get a life instead of sitting in front of the TV all day and watching all this 9/11 tamasha with a disgusted look. If only he was a committed peacenik like me, he could be enjoying in Bombay on Judo beach, and running up and down the hills in Gulberg in Kashmir, and buying saris in My Sore. (Mummy says best ones come from there only.)

Peace keh aur bhi faiday hain. I hear servants are soooo much cheaper in India. You give them a 500 rupee tip and they do jhuk-jhuk ke salaam or namaste or whatever it is that they do. Here tau they look as if you've done their insult unless you give at least a thou. I tau am thinking of firing the whole lot of mine and getting everyone from over there only. Nice-nice Biharis, sweet-sweet Sylhetis. Or are the Sylhetis from Bangladesh? Bhai, whatever! As long as they just do what they're told, I don't care who they are.

If we become all peaceful, I suppose Kashmiris will also become friendly, nahin? And they can start knitting shahtooshes again. Ab tau prices of any decent shawl have gone so high, so high, keh bas. My shawl-wallah told me that it's because the Kashmiris have put down their knitting needles and picked up guns instead. I think so it's very selfish of them, but who listens to anyone these days? Except me. Sometimes I think I'm the only decent, obedient, God-fearing, law-abiding, kindly, nice, honest person left in the whole world. Me and Mummy. Bas.

October 2002

Pakistan, India test missiles
Butterfly goes to sleep

So bore. Nothing's happening. I'm going to sleep till
November.

November 2002

Washington: MMA entering çoalition an 'alarming development'
Butterfly and Mulloo fall out

Mummy's right. It's a curse to be sensitive. Take me only. So much worrying and anxiety I do, keh I can't sleep at night. I told Janoo about my sleepless nights.

'Good!' he said. 'Since you are up all night you can keep watch on the house and we can dismiss the guards.'

'Ji nahin!' I said. 'Do I look like a servant to you? And anyways, I refuse to be the only house in Gulberg without S&M security-wallahs. People'll think we are either kanjoos or can't afford it.'

'You mean SMS?' he asked, grinning like a baboon.

Anyways, to cheer myself up, I went to see Mulloo, who'd just come back from Bangcock. She was sitting in her back veranda, her face covered in asli malai and her head encased in a helmet of mouldy-green drying mehndi. I don't think so she was expecting company. Poor thing, she was never pretty but ab tau, taubah, taubah, one shouldn't say, but she looked like an extra from Kulchoo's favourite film, *Star Wars*.

So I clapped my hands, giggled and said, 'Haw, Mulloo, you look just like an extra from *Star Wars*!

You know, one of those creatures with a trunk like an elephant's and three-three eyes and ears like palm fronds and skin like an alligator's.'

Forgot, Mulloo has no sense of human. Joke tau voh bilkull take hi nahin kar sakti, na. She got so angry that the cream nearly curdled on her face. 'I'll have you know,' she spluttered, 'that all my son's friends call me Yummy Mummy.'

Dil-dil mein, I thought they must be calling her 'Return of the Mummy'. But this time I didn't say in case she bust a blood vessel or something. 'Haw, but why have you put asli malai on your face?' I asked. 'Are you about to eat fruit salad?'

Again she hit the ceiling. 'It's for making—no, keeping—my skin smooth and supple,' she shrieked. 'And if I were you,' she continued, 'I'd buy the Nestlé Milkpak factory to keep you in enough malai to erase those deep trenches you have around your eyes.'

Look at her! Yeh koi baat hai karni vali? And to someone who's so sensitive. My hand flew to my face. 'Oh these tiny, feathery-si lines,' I laughed. 'These are tau only laughter lines.'

'Nothing is *that* funny,' she snapped.

So I stomped out of her house and called Mummy and cried my heart out to her. And thanks God I did. Mummy had just then only heard of a wonderful new medicine that everyone's taking. It's an injection that you put it into your face and all the lines and things vanish, and your face becomes plump and smooth like an inflated cushion. I forget the name of the dawai. Haan, I've remembered, it's called Buttocks. Bus, I'm ordering two crate-fulls tomorrow. And then I'll see what Yoda says!

December 2002

Pakistan fully supporting war against terror: US
Butterfly appalled at unreliability of PIA

You know my friend Moni—haw, bhai, Kasuri, aur
kaun? Whose husband is Foreign Ministry and who
runs Baconhouse School. Anyways, Moni ko tau
Allah ne bachaya hai. She was coming from London
in a plane and as they were driving down the run
away, suddenly there was a loud crash and the whole
plane trembled and quivered like a new bride. And
then the driver braked hard and told all the passengers
that they had to go back because the nose of the plane
had fallen off. Talk of naak katna! So the driver (he
hadn't become the pilot yet, because the plane hadn't
taken off) asked Heathrow Airport if they could give
him a new nose and, of course, goras being the sarrhial
goras that they are, they said that they don't do nose
jobs and particularly not on a Sunday. So the plane
and everyone in it was standed for two days in
London. Just imagine, how Pakistan's naak has truly
been cut by PIA.

But maybe, becharas, they weren't to blame. I'm
sure it must have been Al Qaeda or even RAW who
did our naak katai. I swear...

Or maybe it was Masood. (Voh kaun hai? Hai, bhai, kya ho gya hai? Israeli secretive service nahin hai?) Zaroor, *they* must have done it. They are capable of anything. Everyone says Masood did the Twin Towers and the Pantagone and the Penny Sylvania crash also on 9/11. Also, please don't forget one of the Israeli planes was just fired at, na, in Kenzania or some place in Africa, so this must be their tit for tit. Very laraka they are, that way.

Anyways, I said to Moni, you must give sadqas and read lots of nuffles because really, you've bachoed baal-baal. Imagine what would have happened if the plane's nose had fallen over the sea or something worst. These days tau I feel so unsafe that I don't even leave the house without reading surats and quls five-five times, and blowing hard on myself and Kulchoo. I don't bother with Janoo because he says he is an antagonistic. So why waste my prayers on him, haina? After death I'll go to God and he'll go to Lenin.

But I'm not sure whether even Lenin would bother with him. Voh tau bechara khud, he's fallen on such hard times. I hear no one even gives this much for him in Russia anymore. Nobody bothers to do a khatam or read the Bible at his grave even. At least they could do church service for him and sing carols and hims, vaghera. But no, not even that much they are prepared to do. Vaisay look at the Russians, how ungrateful, haina? These days they are all doing bows in front of that new man, Putting, or is it Yell Skin? Whoever, bhai. I tau damn care. But I didn't tell poor old Janoo all that because I didn't want to make him disheart.

January 2003

US sends desert force to Gulf
Butterfly bemoans the lack of good New Year parties

New Year's was so phhuss. J&S events-wallahs went off to Karachi, and as a consequent there was no big bash in Lahore. All there was were little-little GTs here and there. Azam and Amber had a little dinner, Nuscie and Jeelo had a little dinner, Seema had another little dinner and Ena had yet another little dinner. Bus, we went here and there eating little-little dinners and doing hello-hi. I told Janoo I won't rest till at least fifty peoples have seen my Rizwan Beyg outfit, so we had to party-hop. Janoo kept grumbling but came along because I told him it's New Year's and it comes only once a year and that too right at the end. If I hadn't told him I don't think so he would've known. Also, with what face would I meet Kulchoo next morning if we came home before him?

I belief there was a party at the haveli, oho, baba, Central Party Head Quarters, Yusuf Salli's house in the Old City where everyone from Mick Jagged to Aamer Khan has been intertained (honestly! This much also I have to explain). But it was a bacha bash with a few desperate uncles lurking in the shadows scoping out the teenage girls. There was a tabahi do at Ramzan Sheikh's farm; we were also invited, but Janoo put his feet down and refused to drive through the fog all the way to Bedian near the Indian border at 2 am.

And this morning Mummy woke me up with a call at the creak of dawn saying I must go to hospital immediately, because Uncle Kaukab (whom Janoo calls Uncle Cock-Up) has taken a turn for the worst.

Poor thing! He's Aunty Pussy's husband, na, and in his time such a big shot he was. Tax inspector he was with a big house full of TVs, VCRs, stereos, cars, fridges and servants. He told me once that God helps those who help themselves. And he helped himself for about thirty years to everything that was going. And not even going.

Anyways, when Mush took over and started that accountability tamasha Uncle Cock-Up panicked, quickly sold one house and sent the money abroad. That money Aunty Pussy investigated in a motel in Ontarion started by her cousin. How was she to know that cousin would khao their money? Then the other house, which they'd put on rent, there the tenant became a swatter and wouldn't pay or leave. Uncle Cock-Up threatened the tenant but discovered that although he looked very shareef, with thick glasses and dentures, he was related to a big goonda who runs a huge betting business, and he sent his badmashes to Uncle's house and they dragged him out into the drive away and beat the living headlights out of him. Becharay!

He's in Javed Akram now, and if he doesn't improve we're putting him in Aga Khan. It clean skipped my mind that I'd offered to get him two bottles from

Janoo's sisters. They don't know yet, but the least those two fat cows can do is give some blood to poor Uncle Cock-Up. Main khud hi de deti, because after all he needs blue blood, but kya karoon, I'm so ameanic that I can't even give to an ant.

February 2003

Musharraf asks US and Iraq to give peace a chance
Jonkers re-enters the marriage market

Jonkers was always a problem child. Now he's a problem man. Poor Aunty Pussy is at her split ends. But what to do? Seeing as he's her only son and all. Kiss nay kaha tha to do that marriage of inconvenience with Miss Shumaila, the telephone operator—or was she a secretary? But he is also stuppid and gulliver, I mean gullible. All she had to do was to message his ego a bit with 'Hai, aap kitnay handsome hain, bilkull Amitabh jaisay', and he was eating out of her grubby little hand with the chipped nail polish. And then she had to matkao her polyester-clad hips at him a few times, flatter her eyelashes and bus, he was ready to do nikah with her and hand over everything that his father, Uncle Cock-Up, had cheated so hard to make and Aunty Pussy had fought so hard to hide.

I told him a hundred-hundred times that Miss Shumaila was a gold-dogger and that she was after his money but would he listen? Taubah! Screamed and shouted at me and said I was jealous and cyclical and didn't recognise true love when I saw it. After that I didn't say anything because baba, apni izzat, apnay haath.

'Poori operator nikli,' poor Aunty Pussy told Mummy when Shumaila ran away on the day after the valeema with all the jewellery and things. Aunty Pussy had tried to hide the jewellery in her safe, but Jonkers brought a pistol and threatened to blow his brains out if she didn't give it to him. I told Aunty that she should have let him. What brains does the poor thing have to blow, after all? But back to Miss Shumaila, she didn't even leave Jonkers' keh gold buttons from his sherwani. And oopar say she drove off in the new fully loaded Corolla Salon that Jonkers had gifted to her on the morning after, as moonh dikhai.

Now, museebat, we have to get Jonkers married again. We've seen so many rishtas keh it's not even funny. Sometimes Aunty Pussy ko koi problem hota hai, sometimes Jonkers ko. 'This is not right and that is not right,' they say. Meri tau nerves shatter ho gayee hain. The way they make demands on me, as though I have nothing better to do... It's been at least two weeks since I had a facial, visited my darzi, or had the girls over for a coffee party. Par, majaal hai kay Aunty Pussy zara sa bhi appreciate karein?

On top, Janoo's no help at all. He keeps asking, 'Has Jonkers met his next ex-wife yet?' I swear, he really needs a tight slap.

Anyways, I told Mummy and Aunty Pussy keh we'd better decide Jonkers ka rishta before Muharram, since I'm extremely supercilious and they say it's not a good amen to do rishtas during the month of moaning.

So last evening we went to see Aunty Pussy's sister-in-law's cousin's neighbour's daughter, who's slightly darkish. Also, they're saying she's twenty nine, which means she's at least thirty three. Vaisay tau Jonkers also is thirty seven and twice die-vorced, but he's a man so it doesn't count.

Hai, don't you know about his first marriage, which was to Poncy Mamu's daughter Pinky? She was a bit simple, poor thing, with lots of property but Jonkers is also crack, na, and when Pinky refused to change her name from Pinky Poncy to Pinky Akram, Jonkers threw a fit. Bus, one thing led to another and before even six months had passed, she ran and took a die-vorce. Just like that. Mummy says they probably didn't make any sex appeals to each other.

Then there was Miss Shumaila and now we're looking again. I think so the darkish girl will work out because, becharas, they're not as effluent as Aunty Pussy and all, and you know how poor people get impressed with money and property and things, na.

March 2003

Allies reach Baghdad airport
Butterfly tells the US to shove off

I've chup karaoed everybody—The Old Bag, the Gruesome Twosome, Janoo, even Bush and his English chaprassi, 'Tony the Phoney' as Janoo calls him. I've chup karaoed them with my anti-Iraq war jaloos, which has come on CNN, BBC, even Fox. After all, five thousand women and children marching through Gulberg is no joke. And all khaata-peeta, khandani types, who are doings it for their principals and not for the hundred rupees the rent-a-crowd types get. Nobody can say after this that we Gulberg-wallahs don't stand out and speak up—or was it stand up and speak out? Khair, whatever. Sab ko hum ne impress kar diya hai, and that's that.

At first I wasn't getting involved. You know, na, how I am the shy, retired type. Not at all like those shameless types who are forever pushing themselves forward for every small thing. And also, just between you, me and four walls, I thought in the jaloos it would be just those ten or twenty handloom NGO-walis and Women's Action Forum types, raising naaras and getting arrested. And honestly, one doesn't want to be lumped with that NGO crowd, na, with their undyed hair and their ethnic cloth bags and their dirty silver jewellery. Because, after all, one is different. But then I went to a coffee party at Mulloo's, and everyone there was discussing keh who-who is going and turned out almost everybody was. Haw, hai! How could I be left out of the social scene? So I immediately pushed myself forward and said keh I tau all along was wanting to be one with Iraqis.

On the day I sun-blocked my face, neck and hands, donned a new cotton jora (can't wear silk on jalooses, I'm told, it gets very sweaty), put on my new Channel ki sunglasses with the huge rhinestone Cs, and laced up the bright white Nike boots I'd bought from Al-Fatah the night before. The whole world shook when we marched through Liberty Market raising naaras and posing for TV cameras.

When I got home, I strode into the sitting triumphantly and announced to Janoo where I'd been. He switched off the BBC, stared at me for ten minutes full and finally asked, 'Why?'

So I glared at him and said with my head held high: 'Because main Iraqis keh liye feel karti hoon.'

'Hmm, interesting,' he said. 'More than you've ever felt for Pakistanis, obviously.' And then he looked at my Nikes and said, 'Marching against American imperialism in your new American shoes, I see? Still, I don't mean to belittle your efforts. Well done.'

Sarrhial jaisa.

Only problem is where to go this summers? US is out of question. Poor Mulloo's son, who is at university in Taxes, is having such a tough time keh poocho hi na. His parents have told him, 'Pretend you've got Larry-gitis so you can't speak at all if anyone asks you whose side you are on.' And Kinky's younger sister, who is in an all-girls' college in Messachewsits, is wearing both a big cross round her neck and a bindi on her head so nobody thinks she's Muslim.

But look at that traitor, Tony! Oho, not Mulloo's husband but Blair. How will we go to London now? First thing is, will we get visas? Honestly, so unfair he is! After all the money we've spent in London on flats-shlats, car-vars, shops vaghera, least he could do was let us go and enjoy. Our money's welcome but we are not. Now take Bobo and Baby, you know they spent three million quids on a flat on the backside of someone called Albert Memorial and Bobo bought a Porch, which he keeps garaged in a garage there, which is more expensive than monthly rent for a kothi in Cantt—and now they can't go and use. And why? Because their passports are green and that's not Tony's favourite colour any more. Dekho zara!

April 2003

India slowing peace process: Pakistan
Butterfly plans Kulchoo's birthday party

So bore these weeks are: parties khatam, balls khatam, life khatam. Nothing to keep me going except for a bit of goss here and there. Suna hai, MacDolands ne change hands kar liya hai, but in Lahore only. I'm planning to rent out Main Boulevard branch for Kulchoo's birthday party, but I think so I'll have it transferred into a jungle for a Mowgli themed party. I was telling Mulloo how every aira-vagehra has birthday parties in MacDolands (her daughters Zebunnisa and Falaknuma also had theirs there only), and thora sa difference tau must hai, na, to extinguish myself from the paindu crowd.

'Haw, jaani,' said Mulloo. 'Trust you to think of it. You could switch off the ACs and make it all hot and sweaty and junglee. Then you could also get the management to take the bijli off the bill. What a big saving that will be for you! And instead of going to all the expense of a Kitchen Cuisine ka cake, you could just plonk a bunch of rotten bananas on the table. And also, Kulchoo can wear a red chaddi instead of a decent pair of Ralph Lauren ki kiddies ki jeans. But tell me, what are you going to do about the animals? Inflatable ones from Icchra, that downmarket bazaar where all the penny-pinchers go?'

'Well,' I replied sweetly. 'You've accepted the invitation, so that's Colonel Haathi sorted out, and Zebunnisa will take care of King Loius the ape, and Falaknuma of Balloo the bear... perfect! And Tony bhai is tau a natural Kaa the sssnnake. Really, with friends like you, who needs animals?'

Later I told Janoo and he had a good laugh, but he said not to have the party at MacDolands because they put in too many addictives in the food. 'Haven't you read *Fast Food Nation*?' he asked me.

'Uff! How many of times do I have to tell you I'm not into cookery books?'

Look at all those clueless MNAs who've gone to India to do talks. Musharraf should have sent me instead. So many heart-to-hearts I would have had with designers and jewellers and sari-sellers and hostesses. After all, that's what they want, na? People-to-people contract? Tau bus, one me could have done the work of all those bumbling parliamentarians.

Instead, I went to the Tariq Ali talk with Janoo. Janoo told me it's the first time he's spoken in Lahore since 1969.

'Haw, tau all this time he's been whispering?' I asked.

But I wish I'd gone to Furry's coffee party instead. Her najoomi was coming to read the palms of all the girls there. She had predicated to Furry that she was going to have a surprise visit from someone with very expensive tastes. She got all excited thinking Jemima Khan was going to visit her. Instead, her house got burgled that night.

May 2003

US forces search for Saddam
Butterfly embarks on massive 'girl hunt' for Jonkers

God safe me from family. I said it in front of Janoo, and he said that there was a famous English poet or librarian or something—how you can become famous as librarian, God only knows—who also said that families stuck you up. But mine tau is really driving me around the bends. Ever since Jonkers' wife, that razor-blade Miss Shumaila, left him, Aunty Pussy's been after me to find him a new wife.

'Tum itna bahar aati-jaati ho, you must know thousands of girls for him. You know we're not choosy. Anyone will do.'

Soch-soch keh mera dimagh kharaab ho gya. I mean how many girls can I produce for him? God forbid, God forbid, I'm not some Madam or something, you know. And after all Jonkers, poor thing, hai tau a real shweetoo but he still wears safari suits, aur voh bhi polyester, with no deodorant, and stammers so much, and uss se bhi worst, has no money since that flooze cleaned him out. Finally, after much calibration, I suggested someone new to Aunty Pussy.

Okay, I accept she's an elderly girl, thirty two or whereabouts, but comes from a theek-thaak family, not exactly khatay-peetay but theek-thaak. Father was middling-sa officer at Shells or Uni-Leavers, or maybe ICI even. Anyways, it was multinationalist company. Girl went to Convent. Of course, senior to me by many years. Not a craving beauty or anything, but nice in a simple-sa way. (But then, Jonkers is also not Shahrukh Khan.) When I suggested her to Aunty Pussy, she hit the ceiling.

'You think my Jonkers is so desperate that he'll marry an aged nobody from nowhere?' she shouted. And then she banged on and on about this girl's problem with her biographical clock.

What the clock had to do with the girl I don't know, but I said, 'Take her clock to Kronos Time Centre on the Mall only. They're expensive but they can fix anything. They even did Daddy's grandfather. Clock, I mean.'

Then I told her keh better do the wedding in the summers only, because nobody's getting visa for London so you have a captive audience. 'I'll ask J&S event managers for a nice-si cut price theme,' I said. 'For instant, "Kabhi Khushi Kabhi Gham" would be so appropriate for Jonkers.'

Us peh tau Aunty Pussy just lost it. Not over the theme, but the expense. 'What do you think this is?' she yelled. 'The opening of a new hotel?'

'Haw, Aunty,' I replied, 'in your times, the olden times I mean, it may have been okay to cook a deg and have a ladies-only milaad and chalo, shaadi ho gayee. But ab nahin chalta. These days you can't even open an envelope, let alone a hotel, without an event manager. Didn't I tell you I had Kulchoo's birthday done by them also?'

June 2003

47 killed in Quetta mosque attack
Butterfly's neighbours burgled

You know what's happened, na? Our neighbours got thieves last night. Promise by God. They came in at fajar time, tied up the night watchman (they are poorish, you see, not like us who have proper security types with Kalashnikovs and khaki uniforms), herded the whole family, kids, shids, everyone, into the sitting room at gunpoint. And while the family sat quietly and watched, the chors cleaned them out. Took everything. Computers and DVD and TV and jewellery and silver and all the cash-vash—everything they took. Even their mobile phones they took. Everything they loaded into a van they'd brought, which they'd parked in the drive only. Imagine, right next door to our drive all this was happening.

When they'd finished, the chors sat down the terrified family and said to them, 'Vaisay we are very disappointed in you as a family.' While they sat there mutely, not daring to breathe, the chief chor says, 'Aren't you going to ask why?'

The father and mother exchanged glances and then the father stammered out, 'W-why?'

So the chor gestured towards them all with his gun and said, 'Have you looked at the way you're dressed? Specially your daughters? Wearing nighties, and those too, half-sleeved? Haven't you thought how you will look if thieves came to your house? Luckily we are not the kind who will treat you badly or punish you for not being dressed properly in Muslim way, but times are bad these days. You should take more care.'

And then they said khuda hafiz and left.

So today I called Mulloo and told her.

'I tau sleep in high-necked, long-sleeved shalwar kameez with my hijab tied tightly under my chin, and so do my daughters, Zebunnisa and Falaknuma,' she said. 'The chor was absolutely right, times are bad.'

So I charged into Janoo's study and yelled at him that instead of two-two S&M guards, I want four-four at night. 'And instead of obsessing about the war on tourism and weapons of mass distraction and Guacamole Bay thousands of miles away, you should be paying more attention to what's going on in your neighbour's house.'

But thanks God I didn't have too big a fight with him, because it expired later that he's just put a down payment on a house in the hills. Now that he refuses to go to London and New York he's buying a house in the hills, finally.

Except that it's not in nice, desirable Nathia, but in dull old Changla where no one goes. When I discovered, I hit the fan. 'But the in crowd is all in Nathia!' I yelled.

'That's precisely why I've bought in Changla Galli,' he smirked.

'How did you find anything in Godfortaken Changla?' I asked.

'Serendipity,' he said.

'Who's she?' I screamed.

'No one you are ever likely to know,' he replied.

Must be some cheapster like Jonkers' Miss Shumaila. What else can you expect from losers like them?

July 2003

American forces hunt for WMDs in Iraq
Janoo kills Butterfly's plans for a beautiful summer

'Bore, bore, bore! That's what I am,' I told Janoo yesterday.

'I quite agree with you,' he replied with his sarrha hua smug-sa smile. 'You are an awful bore.'

'*I* am not bore,' I screamed, 'life is bore. No visas to London and no visas to New York, no visas nowhere. All I can do is sit here and sarrho and die in this horrible clammy heat.'

'But you have a perfectly lovely cottage perched on a hilltop at the edge of a pine forest in Changla Galli,' he argued in that argumentative way of his. 'If only you could see it for the gorgeous place that it is.'

'Gorgeous, your head!' I said. 'Why can't you be like everyone else and buy a kothi in Nathia instead of a hut in Changla? That way I could have met the same people that I meet every day for coffee, lunch and dinner in Lahore, and so nice it would have been.'

Janoo's only purpose in life, I think so, is to spoil my life.

Had he bothered to get me a place in Nathia, I could have gone roaring up the twisted hill roads in our Land Cruiser, exhaust blowing, music blaring and all the windows up to show that even in Nathia I can't live without AC. I'd be sitting in the back with my Versace shades and silk kurti over tight jeans, diamond tops glinting, hair blowing lightly in the breeze—sorry, forgot windows are up, so hairs can't blow—latest copy of *Vogue* lying open beside me, so everyone knows I'm parha-likha, and Filipina maid in the dicky surrounded by Samsonight suitcases—latest-wallay, obviously—and Kitchen Cuisine cartons and massive bottles of Nestlay ka pani. And on our backside, a small Suzuki following with our cook and sweeper. Baba, if I don't have my bathroom washed down every day I tau can't go. So sweeper is must.

But I'm damned if I'm creeping off to Changla with nobody to watch and nobody to make jay. Much rather stay puts. Janoo, of course, is threatening to go off with Kulchoo. Go a thousand times, I told him, for all I care. Get off my nerves. It's all his fault anyways that I'm stuck here for the whole of the summers. Anybody who had a little bit of get up and go has got up and gone to London. All you had to do, I told Janoo, is to maro your hands and feet a bit and we'd also be sitting in Royal China in Baker Street where all the Sindhis and Karachiites go to have dimp sump, instead of which I'm stuck in Main Market. How else, do you think, everyone else has got visa? After all, Bunny's been, Sadia's been, Rabia's been, Amina's been—and Janoo says I can't go. Bhai, why? Because he says he refuses to gravel in front of the goras for a visa. As if he was some Nawab Sahib's son who can't lower himself by gravelling like everyone else. Donkey. Dog. Crack. Kameena.

August 2003

Israel refuses to allow Palestinian refugees to return
Butterfly does London

Finally, we've made it to London. Sales-shales are all finished but I'd warned Janoo from before only that sales or no sales, Dior ka saddle bag must hai for me.

'A saddlebag? What's that?' he asked in that weary, half-ill voice of his.

'A handbag, baba, what else? Or "purrss", as your mother would call it.'

'What does it look like?'

'How should I know? All I know is that Mulloo says everyone who's anyone's got it.' And that's reason enough to buy it.

So yesterday as soon as I got out of taxi and into flat and put my suitcases down, I went straight to Harrods. Poor things, Dodie and Diana were there in the window. Big-big portraits with lots of flowers. Itna main ne feel kiya, na, I can't even tell. Stood and said prayers for them. Then I wanted to do something in remembrance of Diana and suddenly I remembered how much she used to love shopping. Tau phir I went in and daba keh, na, main ne shopping ki. Every time I bought something I thought of her. Dior bag, her favourite make. Four pink Channel ki lipsticks, just like she used to wear. Versace dark glasses, like she wore to Versace's funeral. Goochy high heels, in size six like her. Six pairs. Just my little way of keeping her memory alive.

Bumped into Mehreen in the beauty hall, by the Easter Lauder ka stand. Bhai, Mehreen Moodi, who else? They're here to drop their kids off at college, na. Like Haroon and Sadia. And the Lakhanis also. Now that American visas are so hard to come by, people are turning to England universities. Even though they don't give financial aids.

Vaisay sometimes I wonder whether Kulchoo should even go to college. Itna strange ho gya hai, na. Last week he went on at me about some carnival in a place called Nodding Hill in London. I asked around and found to my horror keh it's some kind of African ki demonstration. I had no intention of sending him, but Janoo as usual took his sides and said it was culturally expending and took him off.

So I also went off to do some cultural expension myself. I went to see *Bollywood Dreams*. Hai, so nice it was, itna enjoy kiya, na, main ne. I tell you, there's no one like AR Rahman, particularly now that he's a Muslim.

Next day Janoo asked if I wanted to come with him and Kulchoo to see some stuppid-si exhibition in a place called National Portraits Gallery and then something else at British ka Museum. But I thought, kya time waste karna? Instead I went with my friend Bunty to Royal China on Baker Street where Karisma Kapoor had lunch last week. Voh tau nahin thi but lots of Sindhis were there, flashing diamond nuggets and Channel ki glasses. So flashy they are. I had chicken corn soup, egg fried rice and prawn sweet-and-sour. Shouldn't say because it sounds ungrateful, but Dynasty in Lahore is better. Less pheeka. And now that I've done everything that I'd come to do in London I can go back. Right in time for Muddy Hashwani's wedding in Isloo and Dubai.

September 2003

US concerned about Afghan border security
Butterfly concerned about her missing bike

I swear these poor peoples are so illiterate. So ignorant. On top, they never even listen. Who? Oho, servants, baba! Who else? For years, I've told Aslam (the cook, bhai) till my voice has gone horse to stop having children one on top of the other. Did he listen? Taubah karo. Why should he? After all, I'm providing the quarter, the roti-kapra, the gas-bijli-water. And all the food from the kitchen that he steals also—a chicken and a milk carton here, a sack of rice and a bag of sugar there. And then Janoo pays for his children's school and for their books also. Aslam tau must be a millionaire by now. His whole celery goes straight into his pocket, all six thou of it.

He'd worked with The Old Bag, Janoo's mother, na, ever since he was a child. His father was their masaalchi. So when we got married he came in my trousers, I mean trousseau. I tried to get rid of him many times, because he used to spy on me and report everything to The Old Bag and the Gruesome Twosome.

'Today they cooked this, costing that much, and tomorrow they are expecting so-and-so, and Begum

Sahib waked at this time, and Sahib went out that time,' and on and on and on.

But Janoo wouldn't allow me to sock, sorry, sack him. 'You think he's a spy and a fifth columnist, don't you?' he asked me.

'Who, me?' I asked innocently, wondering who the other four communists were.

Anyways, in ten years Aslam managed to have six children while Janoo and I only managed Kulchoo. Mummy and Aunty Pussy know all about these peoples. They say they think about 'That Thing Only' and that's why they have so many children. Not like us, who've got so many things on our mind and so many worries.

Now Aslam's second son, eight-year-old Billa, has gone and got lost, along with the cycle I'd provided for trips to the market. I mean, just look at them! They send the child out on *my* bicycle without even my permission, and at 7:30 pm so that it'd be dark and the guard couldn't see who was taking the cycle. And what for? To get a midwife from the market because Madam is too scared to tell me she's having a miscarriage. On the way, the kid fell into a ditch, damaged the cycle, searched his pockets and discovered he'd lost the five-hundred-rupee note advanced payment to the midwife. So he went crying to the fruit-seller at the entrance to the bazaar.

'How can I go home now?' he cried to the fruit-seller. Then he took the cycle and wondered off into the night. That much we learnt from the fruit-seller.

That was five days ago. Billa hasn't been seen since and neither has the cycle. Aslam and Madam are wailing all day long, the food's being cooked by the bearer or being sent for from Dynasty Chinese or Punjab Club. On top, Janoo's accusing me of insensitivity.

'It's all my fault, I suppose,' I shouted. 'I tau at least tried to put her on the pill. Did you ever try and get him to use condominiums? Or get his bits snipped off?'

PS—While I was writing this inside, there was a big fuss outside and it respired that Billa had been found. He'd gone to Janoo's mother's house and was skulking around there in her servants' quarters, too scared to come home and tell about the broken bike and the lost money. And look at her servants, so mean they are, they never even told! For five whole days they were hiding him and they didn't tell. When The Old Bag returned from Sharkpur today she found him there and brought him over. Now she's sitting beaming in our drawing as if she was some big detective like Hercule Parrot or something, and the boy's crept off to his mother, who has probably got another baby in her belly already. Honestly, I tell you, these peoples are also the limit!

October 2003

Pakistan clinches $341m arms deal with Pentagon
Butterfly attends a ball dressed as Suzy Wrong

I just couldn't belief my years when Janoo asked if I
wanted to go to the Latent Rehmatullah Ball in Isloo.
'Are you mad?' I shrieked. 'It's *the* social event of the
year and you're asking if I want to go?'

For my outfit I called Shamael in Karachi and said,
'Hai, please help, na. Please send me an appropriate
outfit?'

So she said she'd send me a Suzy Wrong or somebody's outfit by DHL. I wanted to tell to her that I
don't want to wear secondhand but didn't because
I thought keh Karachi ki top designer hai, mind na
kar jaye. Now let's just hope this Suzy Wrong or
whoever she is doesn't have BO.

Then Aunty Pussy begged me to take Jonkers along
to show him a girl or two. Uff, how bore, I thought,
but chalo, at least we'll be able to go in her big Merc
with gun man and all. Arrive in some style. Not like
riding shamefacedly in Janoo's three-year-old Corolla.
The ball was faaabulous, with red velvet tent, orchids,
and me in my Wrong dress.

Only fly in the ornament was that we had to sit
with Janoo's bore Oxbridge friends, who spent all

evening exchanging long-long, bore-bore stories from their past times about university dawns (I think so they call teachers 'dawns' at Oxbridge) and college porters (they must be luggage carriers like our coolies at airports) and getting the Blues (or was it booze?) in cricket and rowing-showing. And then some loser, who was too poor to afford a car as a student even, started telling about how his cycle had got stolen one night from outside his college. So then I also started on a long story about how our cook pretended that the cycle we'd given him to do the groceries and all had got stolen while he'd been inside the butcher's shop in the bazaar but when I threatened to call the police, he quickly said that maybe the butcher would know and he went and promptly got the bike back.

'You should have threatened the porter or coolie or whatever he was called in your college with the police,' I advised him. 'Always you will find that it's the servants who are at the bottoms of it.'

They all stopped talking and stared. I suppose they hadn't been expecting such a clever respond. I just smiled serenely at all the losers, snapped my crutch bag open, took out my latest Channel lipstick, put it on, snapped my crutch bag shut and patted my Chop Suey outfit. They all suddenly started talking at the same time.

Aunty Pussy says people who go to Cambridge get overeducated and overexcited and become egg-centric. Apparently Oxford doesn't have the same effect. Hai, shweetoo Imran Khan went to Oxford, na. People who go to Oxford are called Oxen. That's all that Janoo has in commons with Imran. That they are both Oxens.

November 2003

I hate my friends. All of them. Every single lying, cheating, two-faced one of them. Why? Because they've stabbed me in the back, that's why. While my innocent, trusting back has been turned on them, they've gone off and re-invented themselves, leaving me high and wry. And worst thing, they're making so much of money on top also.

Mulloo the namaazi has become a party organiser, if you please (she's cornered the market in milaads and bismillahs), Flopsy, who failed every year in Convent and got three pink cards from Mother Andrews for being stuppid, has opened a school and made herself Principle, and even Fluffy, whose house, Mashallah Mention, is on our backside, and whose every coming and going I thought I knew, has become a fashion designer! Quietly-quietly she's gone and installed three darzis in her garage and now she's the owner of 'Fluffy's Fab Fashion House'. This is the same Fluffy whose mother still wears a burqa, and Fluffy, who the first time she came to KC (oho, baba, Kinnaird College, what else?) was dressed in a frock and a shalwar. Aur upar se Janoo's cousin, Faiza, whom I tau vaisay have always called Faeda because she's such a user, who's never slept on anything but charpais, has become a furniture designer and even opened a showroom. Dekho zara memsahibs ko! What cheeks!

So I went straight to Mummy and complained. 'I can't bear it,' I wept. 'If I hear one more time how successful they are and how popular they are and how much of money they are making, I'll kill myself.'

Mummy narrowed her eyes into slits like she does when she's thinking hard and hissed: 'These silly little upstarters. We'll show them.'

'But *how?*' I wailed.

'Why don't you open an art gallery?' Mummy said slowly. Now you know why Mummy was head girl at Sacred Heart Convent? Because she's always been more chalaak than anyone else, that's why.

'All you have to do is to rent an empty kamra,' she said, 'and paint it white. Stick in some lights and put up a few picture hooks and there you are. Art Gallery! And you, Gallery Owner!'

But then we had to think of a name. I suggested Decent Art Gallery, but Mummy said no, it sounded too lower middle class.

'Bonanza?' I said.

'No, too upstartish.'

'Tasveer?'

'Too Urdu medium.'

'Marks & Spencer?'

'Isn't that already taken?'

So after many-many thoughts we finally hit on it. As soon as that was decided I rushed out and had my cards printed. Hai, I'm so proud of them. They are light-se pink, like Rose Petal toilet tissue, and on them it says in curly purple writing: 'Art Attack (new art gallery), Gallery Owner and Arts Council: Mrs Butterfly Khan, expert in modern art and pictures and all.'

December 2003

Libya agrees to denounce WMDs
Butterfly goes polo mad

So much of mazza!! I'm tau going off my rocket with all the parties-sharties, shaadi-vaadis and khaanas galore. And the polo! Voh tau even more better. So many polo functions, and all by special invitation only so that no aera-vagheras could get in. Serves them right, I tell you. Trying to muscle in where they don't belong. Janoo's sisters, the Gruesome Twosome, kept calling, kept calling, begging for tickets. So shameless they are. 'Hai, Bhaijaan, humko bhi le chalein, na,' they pleaded with Janoo.

Janoo, being the sulphate that he is, got them tickets in the VIP enclosure. I tau nearly blew a fused. Particularly after what they did to me last week only.

'Bhabi,' said Cobra, the Elder One, 'Aap ne tau voh fillum dekhi hogi, na, jiss mein apki Mummy star kar rahi hain?'

'Kaun si?' I asked.

'Haw, voh nahin hai, *Return of the Mummy*. Itni hum ne enjoy ki, na, aap ka soch-soch keh.'

So when the tickets arrived, I quietly khiskaowed them from the dining table where Janoo had left them and had them sent to Mummy's with a note that said:

'I know you and Daddy already have two-two each but I thought you might like to take your maid and driver. After all, they are also human beings.'

When Janoo asked, I said, 'What tickets, baba? I tau never saw any expect my own. Cross my heart and hope to die.'

Now let the ugly sisters take a panga with me and see what a tit for tit girl I am.

But what a pity keh no glam Indians showed up at the polo. Itna main look forward kar rahi thi, na, to entertaining Shahrukh Khan and Salman and Hrithik in my new sun room with its pink wall-to-wall and apple-green velvet curtains, sorry, drapes (aaj kal only the aunties say curtains). Chalo, next time. But the Denim and Diamonds Ball was just too much, yaar. All these trendy models and cute-cute polo players—ours vaisay were the best. Indian Captain, Samir Suhag, was okay also but nowhere as cute as our Kublai Khan, who lost his teeth but not the match. Too bad they didn't come wearing their tight-tight jodhpurs and their sweaty shirts. So hot they look in them.

Now next in my diary is Sindh Club Ball, from where I'll rush back for Nazi and Mansha's son's wedding, and then back again to Karachi for the Murree At-a-Late Ball, aur phir the Tapal wedding. I suppose I'll have to drag around the zinda laash— Janoo, who else? But as Mother Andrews at the Convent used to say, we all have our crosses to bare...

January 2004

12 injured in Karachi blasts
Mummy, Aunty Pussy and Jonkers depart for Haj

Mummy's gone on Haj. And Aunty Pussy also. Daddy refused to go, said his summons hadn't come yet. And Uncle Cock-Up tau, poor thing hasn't been same since he got beaten up by those goondas. So they've dragged poor old Jonkers along instead. They had to be accompanied by a male member, I mean, mehram, na. Voh tau must hai, bhai. Otherwise you know what the Saudis are like.

'Cheer up,' I told Jonkers. 'Maybe you'll find a nice namaazi type girl there. I mean after all, the whole world comes there. You're bound to get at least one seedhi-saadhi shareef type in all those teaming millions.'

When I told The Old Bag that Mummy was off to Mecca on Haj she muttered something about cats and nine hundred mice or something. I tau ignored. Best hai to ignore. That seclusion I've reached after so many years of marriage.

I told Mummy to do lots of duas for me, for my health, for my looks, for my social life, my bank account. If I hadn't reminded her she was quite likely to hog God all to herself. Sad to say because she's my mother, but she's like that only. I also told her to bring me a litre of holy water from the holy land. It makes your skin glow, you know, it being holy water from the holy land and all. In fact, I even know someone—bhai, Mulloo's first cousin from her father's side—who was so ill, so ill, that doctors-shoctors, everyone had given up on him. Couldn't speak, couldn't eat, couldn't breathe even, but then someone told his parents they should send for holy water because only that could save him. So of course his parents exported a drum of it—or was it imported? Anyways, the minute it arrived they started pouring it down his throat and you know what? By evening he was not just breathing again, he was eating, drinking, sitting up in bed, chatting, everything! As soon as he got out of hospital he immediately went off to Haj to give thanks.

That was three years ago. Now I think so he is living in a huge, big villa in Dubai, because he'd defaulted on some big-big loans from two or three national banks here and government is after him. But, apart from that small matter, mashallah, he is in the pinks of health and he goes for Haj every year.

Haan, so what was I saying? Yes, what I want Mummy to bring for me from Saudi. Maybe some of those nice glass beads that everyone has on their coffee tables now and, if she got to Jeddah, then a string of Basra pearls. But please, no jah namaazes and those date packets. I have quite enough of those already, thank you. I told her she must be back in time for Basant. Can't wait for all the parties, yaar.

February 2004

Troops prepare for raid in South Waziristan
Butterfly betrayed by family

Mummy's come back from Haj without my holy water. She says she spilt it by mistake, but I don't believe her because she's come back looking ten years younger when everyone else who went in her group is at death's door. There was so much of infections there, na. Flu and diarrhoea and meningitis and pata nahin kya-kya. Funny vaisay how God didn't make sure that nothing happened to the Hajis. Considering they'd come all that way for Him.

You should see poor Aunty Pussy—bilkull bride of Frankenstein, with big-big hulkas under her eyes and skin all lose-lose and pale jaisi—well, as pale as anyone can be with Aunty Pussy's navy-blue complexion. So why should Mummy's face look all smooth and creamy, just like Yeh-Lo (voh Bent Affleck ki girlfriend nahin hai? The one who got the pink diamond, baba)? Haan? If you ask me, she's guzzled all my holy water on the sly. It's all jhooth about spilling-shilling, she's swallowed the whole water cooler herself. She's trying to pull a fast one on me but I know she's drunk it. It's written on her face. And all this after doing Haj! Giving golis to your own children. Imagine! She's also brought me a wooden tasbeeh when I asked for Basra pearls. Well, that's the last time I lend her my waxing-wali and my message girl. Next time she can go to Cuckoo's parlour near Main Market and stand in a line with all the secretaries and phone receptionists herself and see how that feels.

And look at that jerk Jonkers—he went all the way to Haj and he's come back single. What a loser, yaar! Couldn't even find one single girl in four millions Muslims.

I asked him and he said, 'Well, Apa, one million, really.'

I wish he wouldn't call me Apa. He's only two years younger than me and ever since he became bald he looks forty five, which makes me...

'What do you mean one million, you paagal?' I snapped. 'All the newspapers are saying there were four millions?'

'Well, about three quarters were men,' he said.

Aik tau he also is so picky, na.

'And what about the other million?' I asked. 'Were they women or were they something else? Honestly, the older you are getting the more choosy you are becoming. You find fault in everyone. Now what was wrong with the remaining million women?' I asked in exasperation.

'Of those, two thirds were over fifty, I'd say,' he replied scratching his shiny head. 'And of the remaining third, almost all were already married.'

'If you let small things like that stand in your way, you will never be able to find a wife,' I told him.

But I don't give a damn, yaar. He can remain single till the dhows come home. Life is busy enough with

103

March 2004

190 killed in Madrid train explosions
Butterfly wowed by wealthy Indians

I think so it's been the most rocking week in Lahore's history. All the rich and glam Indians have been here for the cricket matches. Vijay Malya came. In his jet. Janoo says Vijay's got the alcohol business in India all wrapped up. Must be in packaging and gift-wrapping. Vaisay, nobody wraps a present like Aunty Pussy.

Talking of which, poor Aunty Pussy and Mummy have been reliving all their pre-Partition mammaries. Aunty Pussy says Maharani Gayatri Devi was very beautiful (she's also come, na), and the famous English photographer Cecil Beating took a picture of her. I was sitting there in the lounge only when they were recalling their other mammaries, poor things, so old and all, na. They say Quaid-e-Azam's wife was very beautiful even though she wasn't a Muslim.

Quaid's daughter also came. Lucky thing lives in Bombay with all the film stars. Dina Wadia, very extinguished looking, all stately and dignified. I think so she looks just like Quaid-e-Azam, Mohammed Ali Jinnah, in a sari. Saw her at Didi's dinner only (oho, bhai, Shahida Saigol, who else?).

Hai, it was so nice to see all the rich-rich, glam-glam Indians. We would've got a complex if we didn't have celebrities of our own. Like Yusuf Salahuddin, who's Lama Iqbal's grandson. I told this glam Indian woman that he's Lama's grandson.

'What?' she said, 'all the way from Tibet?'

And I shrugged and said, 'Must be.'

By the way, I also want a private jet.

Only problem is we're loosing in cricket to the Indians. I asked Janoo: 'How many goals have they done?'

As usual, he got exasperated. Then he slowly explained all about cricket to me. I pretended to listen carefully, but honestly it was so bore I almost fell asleep. All I can remember is that you can play for five days non-stop and still have a draw. And there's a nightwatchman and a duck and some men play in slips.

All the rich Lahoris have been having parties for the Indians. Even the poors like rickshaw drivers have been giving them free rides and, aur tau aur, even Saleem Fabrics, which never gives you even one rupee off, has been giving them massive deductions. Honestly, such big hearts we have. But Mulloo says when we go to India it's not like that. A shopkeeper would rather die than give you a deduction. Their hearts are the size of a matchbox. And ours the size of Lahore Fort.

April 2004

Battles flare as Iraqis pledge resistance
Butterfly pledges allegiance to Bapu

Life is over. The Indians have gone back. The parties have ended. There is no more cricket and no more matches. There's nothing to do and nowhere to go.

But I'm so spired by our neighbours' big-big planes that I've decided to become Indian also. I'm going to get thalis, wear saris, become a vegetarian and put that red stuff in my partition. I'm also chucking my 'Fear & Lovely' because The Look is all dark-dark. My mission in life is to be just like all my new best friends across the border. I've even started speaking like them.

When people say to me why I have started doing all this, I reply, 'Because I am like that only.'

I told Janoo that I'm working on a complete transportation. 'Transformation, you mean,' he scoffed.

'Whatever,' I said softly, soothingly. I am a peacenik like Bapu. Oho, Gandhi, you know, Mohtrama. Like him I won't argue. I won't shout. Just do quiet, peaceful opposition.

I carry coconuts in my Prada ka bag and smash them against the entrance door of every house I visit.

And I've stopped doing salaam. Instead I put my palms together and murmur, 'Hello, ji,' while doing that wobbly head thing.

Stiff cotton saris are a nuisance. All scratchy-scratchy and tight-tight. Kulchoo says I look like an Urdu-speaking ayah but I told him Gandhiji wouldn't like to hear him say hurtful things to his mother. I overheard Janoo and Kulchoo refer to me as 'Kasturba', but I pretended not to notice even though I wanted to scratch their eyes out. Instead I repeated to myself: 'Peace. Ahimsa. Gandhiji.'

Last night for dinner I'd ordered a thin-si, soupy-si daal with white rice and mutter paneer. Spoilt brat Kulchoo took one look at the block-print dastarkhan on the floor and said, 'Whatever happened to the table and where's my cheeseburger and chips?'

'Forget burgers,' I said in my new, gentle, ahmisa way. 'Forget chips. We are becoming homespun from now. This is your dinner. Eat, child, and grow strong.'

'But even the servants don't eat things like this,' protested Kulchoo.

Then he asked Mohammed Hussain, the bearer, what they'd cooked for themselves and the traitor said, 'Aloo gosht, Kulchoo Sahib.' So he had a big dish of piping hot aloo gosht brought to the dastarkhan with fat, disgusting pieces of meat floating in it.

I exclaimed: 'Hai Ram! Chhee-chhee!'

I had to drink all the soupy daal myself, while sitting cross-legged on the floor. Because of Gandhiji I didn't want to waste anything. Next day of course I got the runs—and I don't mean cricket. That was my day of fasting for Janoo's life, like in *Devdas*. Of course the day dragged on and on with the fast, and by evening I was feeling so faint, so faint that I thought my soul had transmigrated already. First I cursed Janoo black and blue but in a gentle, quiet way under my breaths. Then I watched tapes of *Kyunke Saas Bhi Kabhi Bahu Thi*, in which everybody looked like they'd got split skulls because of that red line. Gave me such a thumping headache.

Just as I was going to open my fast with a soupy daal, Janoo said, 'I presume you're going to burn yourself on my funeral pyre when I die.'

And then I remembered that film *Water* and I decided there and then not to be Indian. Which was such a relief, because then I could have a proper iftaar with naan kabab and biryani and koftas and haleem sitting on my proper table on my comfy chair in my tracksuit. And yell and shout to my heart's content. Hai, it's so nice to be meat-eating, shouty Paki.

May 2004

19 soldiers among 28 dead in Kashmir blast
Butterfly goes in search of wealthy Sindhis

Such a coo I've done, such a coo keh not even
Musharraf could have pulled it off. Of course, Janoo's
angels even don't know because he is tau bilkull fed
up with what he calls my 'puerile dementia with all
things Indian'. Best is to leave him aside because he's
like that only.

Haan, as my friend Faiza says, the latest accessory
is not the Prada bag but an Indian slung over the
shoulder. So when Didi and Sally and Minnoo can
have rich-rich Indian friends, why can't I, hain? I am
also not me, bachoo, if I don't hook a big, fat Indian
fish. When it comes to these things, no one is a better
hooker than me, that I can tell you from now only.

So I started my champagne to hook a rich Indian.
I went to Mummy and Aunty Pussy and asked them
who the richest Indians were. They know these things,
na, because once they were Indian also. Before they
were Partitioned. Anyways, Aunty Pussy told me that
richest ones used to be the Maharajas and Nawabs
and things, but now they're all ghareeb and have
charraoed their palaces on rent and moved into little-
little bungalows. The new rich ones, she says, all have

names ending with 'ni'. They are Sindhi, but not like our Khuhros and Pagaros and Mirs and Pirs who have Land Cruisers and land only. They are Hindus. Natch. They have private planes parked in Heathrow and swanky yaks moored off Can. Near Niece, baba. In the South of Spain.

'Families like the Lalvanis and Shivdhisanis and Ambanis,' Aunty Pussy said, 'understand?'

'Of course I understand, Aunty Pussy,' I snapped. 'I'm not a crack, you know. You mean like the Thandapanis and the Jamdanis and Machhardanis, na?'

Aunty Pussy blew out of her nose like she does when her maid asks for a holiday. But I'd had enough, so I left with the 'ni' thing stuck in my head like Mummy's joora pin.

Next day, while Janoo was hearing news on TV, it struck me. The minute Janoo left the house, I frantically called up Mouse in Isloo.

'Can you help me get an Iraqi visa?' I asked. (Mouse knows *everyone* in Isloo.)

'Sure,' she said, 'they're two a penny. But why do you want to go to Iraq now?'

'Uff,' I said, 'don't you know, the grandest Sindhi's there only?'

'What do you want with a Sindhi?' Mouse asked.

'Oh, just to be friends,' I replied airily. 'Is it a crime?'

'I suppose not. But what's a high-profile Sindhi doing in Iraq?'

'Not just high profile, but grandest of the grand,' I smirked.

'Really? And who's that?'

'Grand Ayatollah Ali Al-Sistani.'

June 2004

22 Iraqis die in US air strike
Butterfly disappointed by Imran Khan's divorce

Just got back from Karachi, yaar. So tired, na. Vaisay what a hectic, bootiful weekend. Shahina and Shakil (bhai, Jang newspaper-wallay), their son Ibrahim got married, na, to Khurshid and Zeba Hadi's daughter Sheena. One tabahi function after another. A monsoon flood of people. Everyone who was everyone was there. Even Janoo.

I said to him: 'Note kar rahe ho? This is the way to do things. When Kulchoo gets married I'm going to do same-to-same.'

I'm also going to invite everyone—except Janoo's family, of course. I can see them already, trundling in like a herd of dinosaurs in their moth-eaten kimkhab ghararas and their big-big gold jhoomars and fat-fat karas. Sooo last century. Sooo last millennium. Sooo not invited.

After returning to Lahore, I've gone to a few balls-shawls. Voh tau, as Janoo says, are my meat and drink, na. One was Care only. And the other was not a ball but polo match. By Citizens' Foundry. They do education of poor children. Janoo says it's a very worthy project. He'd know. Being very worthy himself.

Talking of worthies, look at Imran. After all those lectures about Brown Sahibs and corrupt partying elites and how we should all take off our trousers and put on shalwars, he's back on the party scene as if he never went away. And all those lectures about family values and he goes off and gets a die-vorce. I'm not saying that he's not allowed to get a die-vorce, but don't give so many lectures, na, to all those who are. That's all.

Itni main disappoint hui hoon, na, keh don't even ask. I used to do so much of tareef of him when he was standing with Justice Party. And when Janoo used to tell me that a leopard never changes his sports, I used to tell him that you tau are a sarrhial of the first udder who never saw any goods in anyone.

And that Jemima also. Sitting over here all hunched up with a ghoonghat like a naik Parveen and lecturing us on how we should live in joint family systems and how much she loves wearing kurtas and shalloos. And now look at her bouncing around on beaches in a nanga bikini with Who Grant.

But one thing you can't take away from Imran, and that's his hospital. That tau is fantastic, even Janoo agrees. And one thing you can't take away from Jemima, and that's Who Grant. He tau is fantastic, even I agree.

Janoo's just too much. Last few months he's been talking about nothing except politics. Even at Salman Taseer's sixtieth the other day, he was going on and on about kaun aa raha hai, kaun ja raha hai. Loser, he was the only one on Jamali's side. Everyone else was on Musharraf's side. And nobody, but nobody, was on Bush's side. Bush tau got a lot of gaalis. I agreed completely. I told everyone how America is the route of all evil. Everybody hates America and Americans. It's the in thing these days. (Thanks God the America ka Council General wasn't there or visas might have become even more impossible.)

Janoo said, 'Somebody should be charged for what's happened in Abu Ghraib prison.'

'How much do you think they should be charged, Janoo? Crore? Two crores. Or ten, even?'

July 2004

9/11 Commission to implicate Iran
Why, wonders Butterfly, is Janoo so odd?

Haw, look at them. How mean they are, throwing bomb on poor Shock Aziz. Him being prime minister and all, what if he'd died? As I was telling Janoo, thanks God he was saved, bechara, and no damage was done.

'What do you mean, "no damage"?' asked Janoo, in his best sarrhial voice. 'Nine people died and you say no damage was done?'

'But dekho, na, darling, I don't know those people,' I replied reasonably. 'How can you expect me to feel sorry for them?'

'You don't know Shaukat Aziz either,' persisted Janoo, staring at me as if I was a stranger.

'But I feel I do. After all, we know so many of the same people. And I know his old home, City Bank, and I see him on TV. I didn't even know the names of the people who died.'

'Enough!' shouted Janoo, flinging aside his newspaper. 'Enough of these inanities.'

Aik tau these days Janoo's paara has charrooed so much that you say even one small thing and he corrupts like a volcano. I think so it is the heat only.

Kitna kaha tha main ne keh let's go to London, let's go to London, but majaal hai keh meri ek bhi suni ho.

'I don't want to go to Blair's England,' he'd snarled.

He may not want to go to Blair's England but has anyone asked me if I want The Old Bag to stay in my house? She's been sitting on my head now for the last three months while her house is being re-innovated. Why she should want her house re-innovated when she should be thinking of, you know, her next house, I mean the one upstairs, in the clouds? (Aik tau you can't say even, or Janoo gets so upset.) After all, everyone has to go one day—even Mush—but the minute you put the words 'going' and 'The Old Bag' in one sentence, Janoo blows a fuse. Too oversensitive he's become.

'How would you like it if I kept harping on about your mother's imminent death?' he asked me.

'My mother's death is not imminent because she is fifteen years younger than yours,' I replied. 'And she doesn't suffer from "sugar" and "heart" and "blood" like yours does. And nor is she always banging on about "when I am no more" and "after I leave" when she has no intention of leaving for anywhere, EVER!'

'I give up!' said Janoo throwing his hands up in the air. 'There is absolutely no point in talking about human frailty to a person lacking so completely in compassion. Might as well try milking a bull.'

'Who are you calling a bull, ji?' I shouted, following him into the lounge. 'And if I was so lacking in compassion, would I be feeling sorry for Shock Aziz

116

because bombers tried to get him, haan?' I said, standing over his chair with my hands over my hips. 'Why have you gone all quiet now? Tell? And why would I be saying thanks God he was saved if I didn't have the goods of my country at heart, haan? Tell? Nothing to say now, have you?' I took a step back as he rose from his chair, but followed him into the hallway. 'Just because I am right and you are wrong, now you've gone all silent, haan!' As he opened the front door and stepped out, I said, 'Going now, are you?'

He nodded wearily. 'I think I'll lose my mind if I don't go out for a while,' he said quietly and shut the door in my face.

Haw! So rude! And what did I say?

August 2004

Pakistan expects backlash after terrorism crackdown
Butterfly's coffee party destroyed by incontinent sheep

The Old Bag is also charrhoing on my nerves so much these days that I feel like… bas, poocho na. She's gone and embarrassed me so much in front of my coffee party set that I've become the laughing stop among them all.

This is what she did. I've told you, na, that my poor darling shweetoo Kulchoo got ill? Got bronckite-us. Bad cuff and high fever and all. First tau I made him do goggles with salted water, but when that didn't make any difference I took him straight away to Doc Anwar. Anyways, he put him on antibionics and slowly-slowly Kulchoo started getting better. But of course The Old Bag doesn't trust me with her darling grandson's care, and after dropping a truckload of nasty, mean-si hints about 'the right diet' and 'the right cure', she finally came out with it and insisted that we take him to see some crack hakeem of hers in Sharkpur where the lands and all are. But for once, Janoo took my side and told her that Kulchoo was in safe hands and he didn't believe in hakeem-shakeems. Chalo, I thought, that's the end of that.

Obviously not. A few days ago, I was having coffee party in my house—Mulloo, Fluffy, Flopsy and her Toronto cousin Billie, who owns a whole building in My Ami, Sandy of Juicy Juice and my big coo, Anjali from Bombay, whose husband Shekhar went to school with Shahrukh Khan's sister; they were all there. I was wearing a new jora from Karma and my new shoes from the Prada boutique in Dubai. Of course, haven't yet been able to persuade kanjoos Janoo to get me that new diamond-vali Shopard watch but I'm working on it... Anyways, there I was all dressed up with everyone looking at me enwiously.

And then the bearer came stammering into the room after he'd just served the sandwiches, saying, 'Ji, B-b-b-egum Sahibji, Bari B-b-b-egum Sahib...'

And I just knew there and then that The Old Bag had arrived to blacken my face in front of everyone. I just knew it, call it sick sense or whatever. And there she was, larger than life, in her Bata shoes and 150 year old handbag, barging into my sitting room with her driver in toe, who was dragging something on a rope. Imagine my horror when I saw it was a bakra! A real, live, black bakra. Doing baa-baa in my sitting room full of my trendy friends, with all my Noritake china laid out so prettily and heaps of delicate sandwiches.

'Kulchoo must touch it,' The Old Bag announced. 'Call Kulchoo and then after he's touched it we will slaughter it on the driveway.'

I was tau completely frozen outside and I had this smile pasted on my face while inside I was boiling and squirming, sending thousand curses on her oiled head. Through gritted teeth I told her Kulchoo had gone for tuition.

'In that case, I'll wait,' she announced, and plonked her backside on my sofa beside Anjali.

And then to my utter, utter horror, I hear the sound of water running and I turn around and see that the bakra is doing small bathroom on my Bokhara rug, and Fluffy is howling like a hyena because her brand new pink suede Jimmy Shoe sandals are also being splashed, and then the driver pulls hard on the rope to take the bakra out and that stupid beast backs into my coffee table, knocking my Noritake platter off the table and upending a tray of egg mayo sandwiches on Mulloo's Karma-clad lap, and she also starts screaming and the driver starts swearing and the bakra baa-ing.

And over all the commotion I hear The Old Bag say, 'Zara voh chicken patties tau pass karna...'

September 2004

Shaukat Aziz sworn in as 20th PM of Pakistan
Butterfly notices that summers are going

Nothing to report except that summers are going, thanks God, and winters are coming, but I expect you know that also. So really nothing to report.

October 2004

Musharraf meets Manmohan in the US
Butterfly's drawing room goes minimalist

Ek tau so much of thinking I've been doing, na, so much of it, keh mujhay lagta hai as if I'm going to get a brain haemorrhoid. I've been popping Lexxos (oho, baba, Lexotnils) to relax my nerves, but not a jolt of difference they've made. Must be fake, do number ka maal. As a result, all of last week I've spent in such kush makush keh jiss ka koi hisaab hi nahin. Now I know how poor old General Mush must have felt when Bush called him on 9/11. Decisions, decisions, decisions! But at least for him the writing was on the ball, meray liye tau no such luck.

Kya hua hai? Uff, taubah, don't you know? Janoo's friend Habib—bhai, Fida Ali, architect nahin hai, from Karachi only?—well, I heard him overtalking of something called 'minimalism' at a khaana the other day. Apparently it's the 'in' look of kamras and gardens, vaghera, in which dunya ka sub kuch hotay huay bhi you have to pretend that you are bhooka-nanga and have nothing. So your drawing and dining should have only one or two pieces. No glass-fronted almaaris stuffed full of jahezi silver, no Begumi piles of multicoloured silk jamawar cushions, no big-big land-escapes in big-big golden frames, no chandi-layers, no jhoolas and Sindhi furniture, no cut-glass vases and bowls, no porcelain figurines, not even Lladro from Harrods. Curtains can't be swagged and fringed anymore. They all have to be linen and cotton, not velvet and brocade. Even your Bokhara carpets should be rolled up and put in the godown. (Now that mine has goat su-su stains on them, that's just as well, vaisay.)

And if you still have all that ethnic painted furniture, then tau you are a total loser and should retire to Sharkpur where all the losers like Janoo's relatives live. But if you are with it and cool, then you should have a nanga floor—but only if it's wood or limestones. Chips must be immediately uprooted. Prints are out. So no paisleys, and flowers tau are so over keh naam hi na lo. Weaves are in. And that too, in tired, dusty colours like moss, mouse, frog, mud. Flower buffets in crystal vases are out. Dry, thorny branches are in. Walls must be white. Furniture beige. And absolutely no carving-sharving. No curtains. Blinds only. Lamps have to be discreet and modern. Like me.

But what is giving me a brain haemorrhoid is what to display now. Should it be the big Gardener plate or the silver tray? I keep thinking Gardener but it has flowers in the centre and flowers are tau bilkull out. Then again silver is over, but one tray I think so is okay. Habib says the trick to avoiding headaches, and I suppose also to look khaata-peeta, is to circulate your stuff. Phir tau I better put the Gardener plate. At least it is circulate in shape.

November 2004

Shaukat Aziz visits India; Kashmir and pipeline top agenda
Janoo needs shrimp, decides Butterfly

Janoo, I think so, needs to go on Prozac. Ever since the beginning of November, na, he's been going from bed to worst. First tau there was the American election. Bush ki victory ko us ne itna feel kiya hai, na, keh jiss ka koi hisaab hi nahin. I think so he's more upset than Carry even. Just kept shaking his head and muttering, 'How COULD they? How could they vote Bush in?'

'Uff, baba,' I told him finally, 'what's to you? He's their PM, not yours. Why are you eating our heads over it?'

'Because what he does has ramifications for the whole world,' he shouted. 'Look what he's done to Iraq, what he's doing in Guatanamo Bay, what he plans to do in Iran. And for your information, he's a president, not a prime minister!'

Same difference! I muttered to myself. I didn't tell him keh I was also disappointed. Itna main hope kar rahi thi, na, keh Carry would win and then we'd get that shweetoo-sa, young-sa Edwards with his glossy hairs and Tom Cruise smile. But instead we have to stare at that sarha hua buddha sanda, Chainy.

And then just as Janoo had begun to shave again, Yasser Arafat went into a comma. Again, Janoo depression mein chala gya. Sat in front of TV all day, na kaheen aana na jaana, na kissi se milna. Na koi GTs, na koi khaanas, not even any iftaaris for God sake. I wanted to tell Janoo, it's all very sad and everything, but Arafat's not your chacha, you know. But one look at his red-red eyes and gritted teeth and I thought better not say anything, otherwise he himself might go into a comma.

And then on top, Falluja happened. Lo, it was as if the Americans were bombing our house. Janoo tau, bechara, bilkull hi crack ho gya. All day now he spends reading international news things on the Inner Net.

So I thought enough is enough, and I called up a brain ka doctor whose number Mummy gave me. Over the phone I told him that I thought my husband was going mad.

'Why?' he asked me.

'Because he's behaving so strangely,' I said. 'He's lost all interest in life.'

'Please describe his symptoms.'

'Well,' I said, 'where do I start? He won't go to GTs. And he won't take any interest at all in who I met at my coffee parties and what they wore and what they said. And he is least bothered about my best friend's husband's new car, which is bigger and more expensive than ours. And nor does he want to know who went on holiday where and how much of shopping they did and how big their bill was. He isn't interested in Bollywood, not even Shahrukh Khan. He didn't even want to know when I told him that

125

one of our GT crowd Billa had left his wife and run off with his telephone receptionist. Imagine! That's how ill he is. *And* if that wasn't enough, he spends all morning—at least two hours—reading newspapers and all evening reading books. And in his time off he watches TV and shouts at me when I switch the channel from BBC to Fox. I think so you need to give him Prozac.'

'I think,' said the doctor, 'that I need to give him some sympathy.'

'Doctor,' I said, 'you are crack.' And I slammed the phone down.

December 2004

**US weapons for Pakistan will hurt peace talks: India
Butterfly gets central heating**

So many decisions I have to make these days. Like
whether to have the floors pulled up and central
heating put in. So cold it gets now, for at least one full
month. And gas heaters are sooo last millennium.

And whether to tell Mulloo that her maid is having
an affair with Fluffy's driver. I know because my
Filipina, Sandra, saw them. Or whether to wait till
Mulloo's being more obnoxious than usual and then
tell her.

And whether to have my eyebrows lifted and my
neckline lowered.

And whether to send the cake that Psycho sent for
Janoo day before yesterday to The Old Bag as a
birthday present.

And what to wear at the *Good Times* magazine
launch party for which Mira Nayyer is coming, hai,
jiss ne nahin banai thi *Monsoon Marriage?* I think so
she's also made something called *Salaam Vanity* and
Bombay Fear...

Uff, taubah, so much to think about. And then
Janoo says I never think.

January 2005

Tsunami hits Southeast Asia, Sri Lanka, India
Butterfly attends fifteen parties in three days

I've also got such bad kismat. The party season's on my head and I've gone and got bronckite-us. So much of fever I've had. And cuff. And cold. And nothing's helped. The only thing that's helped is a homo. (Pathic, bhai.) Homo-pathics are very in these days. Doctors ko tau koi poochta hi nahin hai. And good thing also: jab poocho antibionics transcribe karr detay hein. Antibionics take karr-karr keh my intesticles have rotted, I swear.

But despite of my illness, I've not missed a single party or shaadi. Because I know how much people look forward kar rahe hotay hain to my coming. So first I went to Sheheryar Ali's wedding. Bara fit scene tha, with fountains and peacocks and jewels to die for. Nice plot they have for a party, vaisay. Big-big, open-open. And the best address in Lahore: 1 FCC.

Then there was that lunch for Sara Guleri. Bhai, jiss ne write kee thi na voh book *Meatless Ways*. She teaches at Yales. She's written a new book called *Boys Should Be Boys*. Lunch was nice but I left before the guest speaker's speech because I didn't want to miss the final episode of *Kyunke Saas Bhi Kabhi Bahu Thi.*

But imagine what happened when I got home? Kulchoo was watching *The Meekest Link* on BBC. I told him to switch it off but he said first I had to buy him a Sony Flatron for his room. Look at him! When did he get so materialistic? So matlabi? Where does he learn it from? Must be school only. Everything bad comes from there only.

Anyways. Then there was Ahmad Rashid's Christmas party, full of left-wings-wallay, you know, Rashid Rehman, Najam Sethi, Ijaz-ul-Hasan, and the whole NGO crowd. Wearing khaddar and talking bore-bore things like politics and econmics. Food was good, but. Turkey and lamb roast and crispy salads with lovely dressing gowns.

After lunch mujhay thori si weakness ho rahi thi, but then I took two of my homo pills and drove out to Bali's Bedian bash. Everybody was there, including Shaukat and Marina. (Bhai, voh New York wallay.) I hear she knows everybody who's everybody, including Coffee Annan, Moody Allen and Paris Sheraton, sorry, Hilton. Main nay daba keh PR kee, rushed around saying hello to everyone—even those I didn't know, because I thought if they are at Bali's they must be important or rich or both. Preferably both.

February 2005

Musharraf pledges to hunt Uzbek militants
Butterfly gets tricked by her cook

Ek tau this tsumani is also not stopping. Now it's also come into our house. Taken off all our servants and all our clothes. It began with the new Bingo cook, Qamar-ul-Islam (didn't I tell you I finally managed to get rid off Aslam, The Old Bag's agent? He went back to her only). Qamar came and told me the wave carried off his entire village and he must go back home just now only to find his family, all of which is missing.

'Six daughters, five sons-in-law, four sons, four daughters-in-law, 25 grandchildren and one wife, all missing?' I asked.

'Yes, Begumshobji,' he cried, dabbing at his eyes with his apron. 'All missing. House gone, family gone, cattle gone, life gone.'

First tau I felt like saying, 'And who's going to cook the big khaana I'm having for forty people next week?' But then I thought of Janoo sitting in front of the TV, shaking his head, and muttering, 'What a disaster!' At the time I'd thought he was talking about The Old Bag, who is a walking-talking disaster, but later I realised he meant the tsumani. So I put a big pathar on my heart and said to Qamar that he could go but first I must check with Sahib.

'No, Begumshobji, let me go just now only,' he pleaded. 'I beg you.'

So, being the saint that I am, I retented, and on top gave him twenty thou also to help rebuild his house. He left grinning from ear to ear. It made me feel so good, na, helping the needy like that. I swear I felt jannat ki hawa on my face.

When Janoo came home I told him of the big sacrifice I'd made. 'Qamar's gone,' I said.

'Where?'

'To East Pakistan.'

'You mean Bangladesh.'

'Whatever,' I replied airily.

'Why?'

'Because I think so we gave them freedom. And they chose a new name.'

'Not Bangladesh,' snapped Janoo. 'Qamar. Why's he gone?'

'Because,' I said, speaking very slowly as if to a retarded child, 'his village has been swept away by the tsumani. And his whole family's missing.'

'The only thing that's missing,' shouted Janoo, 'is your brain. Don't you ever listen to the news? The tsunami never got to Bangladesh!'

So when Sandra, my Filipina, came and said she wanted to take early chutti and go home to Vanilla, I blew a fuse. 'I suppose your family's missing also. Well, missing or not, no one is going from here till I say so.'

Then on top, at Kulchoo's school they've asked for donations for the tsumani victims. Can be anything—

money, kapras, blankets, food, Kulchoo said. Pehlay tau I told him we'd already bought our qurbani ka bakra and that's our donation done and delivered. But then he told me Fluffy's son brought lots of clothes and tins of food, all packed by his mother in a neat brown parcel. Since Janoo is always doing burh-burh about my having too much of clothes, I thought chalo, let's get rid of all the ugly stuff I received at my wedding from The Old Bag. So I packed up a huge sack full of clothes: horrid old kaam-wallay ghararay and kimkhab ke churidars and tissue ki saris and golden platform sandals and, best of all, Janoo's grandfather's shaadi ki kimkhab ki achkan. Teach him to shout at me again! On top I also sent the bakra to the school. They can ship him off to Nepal, which I hear has been worst struck by the water.

But what to do about the lunch? I think so I'll just cancel it. Anyways, it was only Janoo's family. They can all do with skipping a meal, obese jaisay cheapsters. I'll tell them that I'm donating the money from the lunch to the tsumani revivors.

March 2005

US agrees to sell F16s to Pakistan
Butterfly ponders the merits of a hair transplant

Haw, look at Shahbaz Sharif! Or actually, don't! You may not recognise him with his new hairs. Dekho zara, ex-thief minister, sorry, sorry, I meant chief minister. Honestly, kya ho gya hai mujhay? Tomorrow I'll forget my own name. Janoo says it's the onset of premature dementia. Ji nahin, I said, premature ho gay tum. I tau am always fashionably late. Anyways, so where was I? Haan, Shahbaz! I'd forgotten he'd had a hair transport until he announced his third marriage. I thought only young men—like in their twenties, baba—who start going bald and can't nail rishtas, get new hair. Not senior citizens. But then I suppose if you're marrying another senior citizen then you want to show, na, that there is still lots of dum in you.

But what I want to know is why Nawaz Sharif has also gone and got a rug on his head? He's not getting married again. Or is he? You never know with men, vaisay. Men can do anything anytime. That's what Mummy says. Not that poor old Daddy has ever done anything. He tau doesn't even dye his hair. But so nice he looks, na, so nice, with his grey-grey-se baal to match his grey-grey-si outlook. For that matter, even Janoo looks a bit like Richard Gayer. But bechara doesn't have the body, or the crinkly smile. Or even the Pretty Woman, as Janoo himself says.

'No, darling, you tau just have a crinkly face,' I said.

But he does have the grey-grey-se baal. That much I will give him.

Anyways, I must dash. Have to go to Isloo, na, to do afsos with General Sahib for fautgi in his family (by the way, who exactly's died?). Lahore tau is wearing such deserted looks these days because everyone is in Isloo doing afsos.

Thanks God for the Lahore Book Fear. If it wasn't for the Indians who've come, Lahore tau would have been totally lonely. Only pity is just the booky types have come. No film stars, no shrieking socialites, no business magnets. Just the quiet librarian types with cloth bags and grimy glasses. Par chalo. Something is better than nothing.

April 2005

**Musharraf and Manmohan push forward peace process
Car loans are hateful: Butterfly**

Summers are coming. Fans are on. Car mein tau AC is must. Vaisay, have you noticed how much of traffic there is on the roads suddenly? Yesterday it took me full hour to get home from Liberty Market. I'd gone to Saleem Fabrics to check out the lawns but it would've been quicker to fly to Dubai and done my shopping there only. Janoo says it's because of all the car loans. The traffic, not the shopping. I know, I said. Every Tom, Dick and Hairy's got a car now. Even my waxing-wali's son's got one.

Honestly, some of these new Suzuki-wallahs don't know how to drive even. Barging in from left, right and centre, taking up our parking spaces and behaving like real upstarters. Yesterday, when one stole my parking space outside Habib Bank just seconds before my driver was turning in there and I stuck my head out of the window and screamed at him, you know what he did? He said, 'This is a public parking lot, not your private plot!' And then slammed his car door and sauntered off, whistling with hands in trouser pockets.

Imagine! The guts! And you know what he looked like? Like one of those clerks, all thin and reedy, who used to quietly, uncomplainingly work for hours and hours in Daddy's outer office where there used to be only punkhas and no ACs. And now they've got cars! And tongues! As Daddy says, 'Bhutto has a lot to answer for!'

Really, they shouldn't be given loans and they shouldn't be allowed to drive! I'm saying for their own goods only. Tomorrow they'll bang up the car and who will pay the loan, hain? They tau will default and it will be tax-paying, shareef citizens like Janoo and me who'll be left with the bill. I said as much to Janoo and in respond he gave me a funny-si look. Let him give! I damn care. He's also such a two-faced hippocrit, na.

Why? Haw, how you can ask? Pehlay when we won the test match he said he was going to watch the one-day in Delhi. Then when we lost the one-days, in Coaching and that other place, Vishakawhatever, he says what's the point? Of going to Delhi!

'Point?' I screamed. 'Point? I'll tell you what's the point. Parties are the point. Seeing is the point. Being seen is the point. Coming on TV is the point. Sarrhoing Mulloo is the point. Enjoying is the point. Shopping is the point.'

Then I told him what's NOT the point. Cricket is NOT the point. Bore thuk-thuk with bat is NOT the point. All those silly mid-offs and square legs and perverse swings and bore-bore things. They are NOT the point.

Well, if I'm not going to Delhi I'm going to Karachi for Habib Fida Ali's birthday party. It's his seventieth and very reclusive too. For a hundred and fifty people only. He's invited Flopsy and she said she'd take me along. But what to give him, yaar? Crystal bowel? But I've heard he likes ethnic. Flopsy says he has miniatures and Gandhara and that sort of stuff. So shall I give kimkhab cushions? Very nice ones they are selling on backside of Ashraf Ali, Qamar Ali. With golden tassles. Or maybe camel-skin lamp. Or how about marble vase? That's ethnic, isn't it? So much of headache. I think so I'll just buy him Versace dark glasses from Agha's only. If it's one thing you can never have enough of, it's Versace dark glasses. And Goochy bags. And diamonds. And plots. And Prados. And servants. And bank accounts. In sterling, but. Baki tau, I'm always doing shukar Allah and all.

May 2005

Lahoris participate in mixed marathon
Janoo goes junglee

Janoo's just come back from a week in the mountains.
Because he hasn't started building on his own plot
yet, he borrowed Mouse and Zaheer's cottage in
Changla Galli (their friends call it 'The Mousetrap'
because it cost a lot and took a long time to complete).
Janoo said he wanted the peace of the hills. I told him
I also want a piece of the hills, but I want a seven-
bedroom kothi on it with servants' quarters and guest
sweet and not a cute-sa cottage. But meri kaun sunta
hai? Anyways, he came back very pleased with himself.
I asked what he did do there and he said he went
for long walks, watched DVDs and read by a log
fire. Loser.

Went to a GT at Mulloo's last night. Dragged Janoo
along just in case people think he's left me. You know
how suspicious people are in this town. Always
thinking the worst.

Of course, the minute we got in Mulloo asked me
in her shrill voice, 'Haw, you didn't go to Changla?
Why, but? There isn't some khutt-putt between you
two, is there?' she said, smiling like a fox who's just
seen a fat, defenceless hen.

'Not at all,' I replied airily. 'It's just that it's simply too bore for me. Take away the mountains, the forests, the waterfalls and the views and what's it got? Nothing!'

And then Janoo, bore that he is, started banging on and on about the joys of Changla and how lovely it is to spend time amid nature. So of course Tony— he is so competitive, na, that he'd strangle his own twin in his mother's stomach—he also started on about all the nature he saw on his last trip abroad. And how it was nicer than the nature that Janoo saw. Cheapster.

'But didn't you go to Bangkok then?' asked Janoo, puzzled.

'Haan, but there also you see the sky and breathe the air. Allah ki shaan is everywhere.'

'But you know,' said Mulloo, in her most tired-si voice. 'We tau have travelled so much, so much, that every place has become bore. Ab dekho, last year Tony dragged me off to Venice. Itna suna tha, itna suna tha keh uss jaisi koi place hi nahin hai, and when we got there, guess what we found? It was all flooded. Couldn't even step out of the hotel room without falling into a river. And that also all brown-brown, dirty water. Imagine! From there we went to Rome and it was all broken-broken. Worse even than Mohenjodaro. That Collerseum of theirs, taubah, so much work it needed doing. Worse than Fluffy's face it was. Thanks God there were some nice shoe shops and bags vaghera in Rome, otherwise tau it would have been total waste. Also there was that nice jewellery shop, Burglary, where I managed to spend a few hours. And then someone suggested we go and

139

see, kya thee voh jagaa, Tony? Haan, Granada, to see that palace. Kya naam hai, bhai, us palace ka?'

'Buckingham?' I suggested.

'Nahin, nahin.'

'White House?'

'Oho, nahin. It's named after that shop in Main Market, baba. Kya hai voh? Alhamra! Haan. I knew it. Dekha? Alhamra Castle. I'm not saying it wasn't nice. Of course all those Islamic buildings and everything are very pretty in their place, but really not so much different to the Lahore Fort, nahin? I mean, why go all that way if you're just going to be greeted by the Fort at the end of it? And uff, so much of rush there. So many people keh koi hisaab hi nahin. I said to Tony, bhai, I tau I am not used to. Take me from here, baba, to my own sakoon-wali kothi in Gulberg. Honestly, East or West, Home is Best. Nahin, Tony?"

'Bilkull,' said Tony. 'Home, and Patpong.'

140

June 2005

PTCL workers go on strike
Butterfly dreams of a weekend farmhouse

I'm so fed up, so tired, so sick to deaf of Janoo and his kanjoos makhi choos ways, na, keh poocho hi na. Only God knows how I've done guzara for all these years with a kanjooshra kameena like him. Honestly, koi aur hoti tau kub ki chhorh-chaarh keh chalee gayee hoti. What's he done now? Aik tau you are also always in a comma.

Bhai, it all started with a tiny-si request from me. You know how down to hearth I am, how I crave the saaf-suthri simple zindagi, deep in my hearts of hearts. So into fresh air I am, so much a lover of green lawns (and not just the Al-karam valon ki) and big-big trees and long-long driveaways and huge-huge farmhouses— no, no, I mean simple-se farmhouses. So I said to Janoo as we were driving back last weekend from one of our friends' places in Bedian how nice it would be to have a chota-sa, cosy-sa farm there also, to which we could invite all our friends from Lahore and have open house and casual GTs with barbecues and born fires. Bas, I said only this much and he blew a phase.

'In case it's escaped your notice,' he said through gritted teeth, as if he had a quinine tablet tucked into his cheek, 'you are the mistress of a sprawling great farm in Sharkpur that you have not deigned to visit for four years, and since you mention a cosy-sa, chota-sa farmhouse, my ancestral home...'

'Oh, that pile of 300-year-old rubble!' I pooh-poohed. 'Only a loser would want to go to that Godforshaken house, which doesn't even have a home cinema or a gym even.'

'It's an authentic haveli, not an ostentatious nouveau mansion with Doric columns and Palladian façades masquerading as a farmhouse!'

'You're just jealous because nobody likes your stupid old Sharkpur or your paindu pastry family or your crumbling old house, while everyone just adores Bedian,' I replied.

Anyways, there was a lot of tu-tu-main-main, and now Janoo and me are not talking.

But imagine what knives walked over my heart when I saw Liz Hurling in Bedian (hai, so nice she looked in that white sari with sequences) with that Arun Nayyer in his crackling shalloo (oho, baba, shalwars), thinking that had I had a farmhouse in Bedian, I too could have invited her and been a dignified-si, salacious-si hostess. And kal ko when Kulchoo got married we could have had a mehndi for him there only. By then all those bore prescriptions that this spoil spot government has put on shaadi festivities and food would also have lifted, and we would have given a big khaana without having to call the mehndi 'rang' and the valeema a 'to meet' ceremony.

But none of my dreams are ever going to come true, and you know why? Because I'm married to a killed joy, kanjoos loser called Janoo—that's why!

July 2005

37 dead as terrorists bomb London
Butterfly wonders whether she will ever get a UK visa again

Look at these spoil spots, these bombers! Going and blowing up the tubes in London. And almost all of them Pakistanis. Honestly! So mean of them, so selfish. The least they could have done was to think of us, sitting here sarrhoing in the heat of Lahore. Already it was so difficult after 4711, I mean, 9/11, for us to get visas to London and New York; now tau it will become impossible. Visa officers will hit hundred-hundred shoes on our heads when we ask.

I'm not saying they shouldn't be allowed to kill themselves—oho, baba, bombers not visa officers. If they want to, they should be our guests, or rather, Allah Mian's guests. No one's stopping them. But they should have the decency to go hang themselves from a tree or jump off a tall building or into a well or whatever. Why take along computers, I mean commuters, who don't want to go, whom you haven't asked even? Haan? Maybe they don't want to go to paradise just yet, nahin?

I asked Janoo. I said, 'Since you're Mr Know-All, please tell this to me. Why are these suicide types such spoil spots, hain?'

He muttered something about cultural animation and econmic delusion and political powerlessness and other bore-bore, stuppid-stuppid things like that, but when he saw me yawning, he said, 'It's like this: they feel that nobody cares about what they think and so they feel ignored and angry. And this is one way of making themselves heard.'

'You mean with a bomb? You mean make such a loud explosion that everyone goes deaf? That way you're going to make people hear the things you want to say?'

And then the more I thought about it, the stranger it seemed to become to me. I mean like if Mulloo didn't invite me to her parties and didn't care about how angry and ignored I felt, would it make sense for me to arrive uninvited to her next do, push myself in with all her guests and then blow myself up in her sitting room? No, because not only would I not be invited to any more parties—because I'd be dead and dead people don't get invited anywhere—but even poor old Kulchoo's social life would also die. Janoo would be unaffected because he tau never had a social life in the first place, but Kulchoo and I would be toast, as they say in Hollywood. Khair, I tau would be toast in more ways than one, but who knows, even Mummy might find herself deluded, I mean excluded, from her bridge group, and even Aunty Pussy might find herself a person non granta.

And Jonkers tau can forget finding another rishta ever. They will say, 'Haw, don't you know, he comes from *that* family, only. The one with suicide bomber. No, baba, too dangerous.'

And also, as I pointed out to Janoo, if I kill the same people that I want to be invited by, then who's left to invite me, hain?

For once he agreed with me. 'Well, yes,' he said. 'You do have a point.'

Honestly, so simple and straightforward it is. If only the bombers had consulted me before, none of this would have happened and we would all have been fine with visas in pockets and Pakistan's rep—oho, baba, *reputation*—intact. I think so, I should set myself up as consultant. Bomb consultant and explosives expert. *Kaisa?* Maybe I should put that in the bit where it says 'profession' in the passport. It would impress the hell out of visa officers, nahin?

August 2005

Jihadis running for local elections
Butterfly's darzi departs

He's left me! Dekho zara! Imagine, after all these years, after all I've done for him, he's gone without even a backward squint. Who knew his name, even? Hain? Tell? I brought him out, I made him famous. And this is how he replays me. Mummy was right: Never trust a man. He'll always double-cross you in the end. Leave you hanging high and fly. Aadmi zaat is like this only. He's gone to Dubai. Thinks he's going to make it big there. Who does he think he is? Some Russian senorita with golden hairs and blue-blue eyes?

Once my Iraqi dinars make me rich, my jooti won't even care. I've bought so many-many, and that too dirt cheap, that I'll be the world's richest person. I won't even be needing the Grand Ayatollah Sistani to maro show. I'll also become a famous oil magnet, a typhoon like John Paul Betty or even Bill Gates. I called Mummy and poured out my brain to her. Didn't take very long. But Mummy koh dekho, so selfish she's become. Majaal hai keh zara bhi sympathise karein? Any other mother would have been so heart warning.

'Don't you think you're overreacting to his departure?' she said. 'After all, he was only your darzi.'

'*Darzi?*' I screeched. '*Darzi?* Master Bashir wasn't just a darzi. He was my *shrimp*. I used to tell him everything and he used to advise. You know how he used to bring his machine and come and sit in the house and watch all the aana-jaanas with his beady little eyes and then advise me on how to kaato the pattas of The Old Bag and the Gruesome Twosome. And he was my spy. If it wasn't for him, how would I have known that Mulloo's husband's car was seen parked outside a new house in XX Block in Defence four nights in a row when Mulloo had gone shopping to Singapore? Also, who will sow my sari blouses in the Kajol-style now?'

'I know, I know,' she soothed, 'but I still think you're over reac...'

'Over? Me? Over? What do you think you are in your maroon platforms and maroon jora and maroon hair? Over! That's what. So, so over!'

Silence. And then Mummy said in a tight little voice. 'I think after this little outburst you and I are also over.' Click. She'd hung up.

Uff! Aik tau after her memo pause Mummy's also become so sensitive. Zara sa bhi kuch keh do, tau she flies off the candle. Now I suppose I'll have to go and manao her with a Swiss voile ka jora. And then I'll have to khiskhao Master Ramzan from Fanny—bhai, nahin hai that smart-si woman, Farnaz. So much of jaasoosi I'll have to do, so underhand I'll have to be and so much of expense I'll have to go through. Janoo will hit the ceiling. Better call Mulloo first and find out if they've found oil in Iraq yet.

September 2005

Hurricane Katrina strikes New Orleans
Jonkers wins Butterfly's respect

You know, na, that I've always thought Jonkers was a bit of a bonga, a loser, a bechara. Dekho zara, Mummy has me—sophisty, smart, connected—and poor Aunty Pussy has Jonkers—shy, shabby, disconnected. I mean, koi comparison ho sakta hai? From anywhere? But then this dakoo thing happened and I tell you, he went up a hundred-hundred times in my steam. So much of ghairat he has, so much of honour. I tell you, he's kept the whole family's izzat.

Haw, what do you mean, 'Which dakoo thing?' Which planet are you living on, baba? The sun?

You know, na, that Aunty Pussy and Uncle Cock-Up had gone to Peshawar for some fautgi last week? Bhai, Jonker's paternalistic family is from there, na. So Jonkers, who as everyone knows is between marriages once again, was all alone at home. Anyways, the servants had given him dinner and gone off to their quarters. (Aik tau they have also become so kaamchor, running off at the smallest excuse to watch TV in their quarters. I tell you, their celeries should be halved.) Anyways, Jonkers hadn't got anywhere to go, even though it was Saturday night, so he'd gone to sleep. Bechara, such a social failure he is, not like us who have to refuse 20-20 invites every night.

In the middle of the night, he felt someone pushing him roughly. At first tau he just mumbled and rolled over because, poor thing, he's being used to being pushed around, but when he felt something hard pressed against his forehead, he woke up with a jolt. He reached for his glasses and put them on and discovered that there were four dakoos in his room. One, kameena jaisa, had put a devolver to Jonkers' forehead and was demanding that he open his safe. And he was not using very nice language also. No 'please', no 'kindly', nothing. Pehlay tau Jonkers nearly fainted with fright but when they grabbed him by his pajama jacket ka neck and marched him to the safe, Jonkers, poor thing, compiled.

Thanks God, Aunty Pussy is a kanjoos who never ever airs her jewellery (or whatever's left of it, after Miss Shumaila ran off with all that stuff), so that was all safe in her American Express locker. When Jonkers finally managed to open the safe with trembling fingers and a gun prodding him in the back, he found a single brown lifafa. The chors ripped open the lifafa and discovered only a pathetic 5000 rupees in it!

'Only five thou?' smeared the chors. 'And you call yourself a seth?'

Now, so far all of this badtameezi Jonkers had taken in his usual chup-chaap, shareef way. But now tau his blood boiled. This was too much. Imagine! Questioning his seth-ness.

'How dare you?' he shouted. 'Take me to your car at once!' (He would have used *his* car, but Aunty

149

Pussy had gone on it to Peshawar.) Riding with the dakoos in his striped pajamas and slippers, he took them straight to an ATM and took out all the money he had in it (I think so, kam-az-kam, fifty thou). He slapped the crispy notes in the hand of the chief thief and shouted, 'Here! A present from a seth!'

Ab Jonkers ko admire na karoon, tau kya karoon?

October 2005

**Pakistan's worst ever earthquake devastates thousands
Butterfly sacks her maid**

I'm firing Shanaz. Bhai, my maid, you know the one who was called Shameem but Mummy changed her name to Shanaz because she didn't want the maid to share her name, otherwise how was she going to call her 'Bewaqoof Shameem!' Yes, that one only! You know what she's gone and done now? Shanaz, baba, not Mummy.

Mulloo called up yesterday after lunch. Shanaz picked up the phone and when Mulloo asked, 'Begum Sahib kya kar rahi hain?' she replied, 'Voh paat par bethi, su-su kar rahi hain.'

Imagine!! I heard her with my own years from the bathroom. I tau nearly had a cease fire—sorry, I mean seizure. Honestly, these people are so crude! So I charged out of the bathroom like a heat-seeking missile and, grabbing her by the wrist, hissed: 'How many times I've told you that if someone calls and I'm in the bathroom you are to say that I'm taking a shower?'

'But you weren't taking a shower, you were doing su-su, I could hear it through the door!' she whined.

'I'm never doing su-su, you understand?' I screamed. 'I'm never doing su-su or anything else on the pot. I NEVER sit on the pot. I only ever take a shower or wash my hands. Yes, you can say I'm doing vuzoo for namaaz if Sahib's mother calls. But I'm never doing su-su. Never, ever!!' And then I sacked her.

Haw, look at this earthquake. So bad, na. We were watching it on TV last night, all those people sitting outside their wrecked homes, when Kulchoo came into the room and gave Janoo a lifafa.

'What's this?' asked Janoo.

'My pocket money and all the Eidi that I've saved. I want you to send it to the people who've been affected by the earthquake.'

So Janoo hugged him and promised to send it right away. And then he said that he would hire a truck and fill it up with medicines and blankets and food and water and powdered milk, and he'd take it up to the mountains himself.

So Kulchoo looked at me and said, 'And you, Mummy, what will you do?'

'Me? I'll call up Mulloo, Fluffy, vaghera and tell them how much we've given.'

November 2005

Commonwealth summit warns Musharraf over uniform
Butterfly celebrates Halloween

Janoo, I think so, is having nervous breakout. All day, all night, he rants about bore-bore things like Talibans and Al Qaedas and jihadis and wahabis and suicide bombers and ISI and God knows what-what else. He says fundos are everywhere and while Gulberg and Defence-wallahs are attending fashion shows and planning weddings, they are quietly organising the biggest GT ever, which, whether we like it or not, whole country will have to attend.

'You watch!' he says. 'You just watch!'

At first tau I ignored, but after a while he got so much on my nerves with his damn fool fatwas that I also exploded. 'Uff, baba,' I screamed, 'if I hear Al Qaeda-Shaeda one more time, I'll scream.'

'You're already screaming,' he said quietly.

'So where are your Taliban, under this table? Where are your bombers, behind this sofa? ISI in the cupboard? For God's sake, they are in Waziristan, a thousand miles away. No one is in Lahore. Gulberg is safe, safe, safe. Okay?'

'Dilli door-ast,' he said wearily.

See? Crack hai keh nahin? Here I am talking of Waziristan and he's banging on about Delhi.

I called Mummy and she said he must have had kala jadoo done on him and I must immediately give bakra and have Quran read. So I sent the driver to the local mosque where the Maulvi Sahib wears a green turban with a long tail, and paid him to do a Quran reading in our names. Obviously I didn't tell Janoo, and nor did I tell him that I'd given The Old Bag some dosh also to do bakra in Sharkpur in his name. You know what he's like, na. Communist jaisa.

Anyways, to cheer myself up after that I organised a Holloween party. After all I'm also human being, no? Got a party organiser—sweet-si girl who Flopsy knows—to do up house. She went and draped it with cobwebs and put big hairy-se spiders who look just like The Old Bag and splashes of fake blood on the walls and brooms and melting candles. I made the servants dress in black with ashes put in their hair. I also told guests they must dress scarey-scarey. Mulloo asked what she should wear and I told her to come as she was, because she looked like a witch anyways. I don't think so she's coming any more. God knows why.

Party was at 11 and at 8, bell rings and who should walk in but The Old Bag. Straight from Sharkpur to tell me about the bakra. Bearer opened the door in his torn black clothes and ashy hair. The Old Bag took one look at his face and then behind him at the blood-splashed walls and cobwebs and dark-dark lightning and she screamed, 'Ya Allah bachaa!' And she pulled out her tasbeeh from her bag and started purrhoing and phookoing and backing away from the door. Kulchoo came just then, but he was also dressed as skeleton and when she saw him she tau passed out. So I had her sent home like that only. It took four men to lift her and put her in the car and I had a *lovely* Holloween party.

December 2005

Musharraf for Islamic renaissance
Butterfly buys fake Rolexes

There's to be a dinner at our house. Big sa, boring sa. With whole of Janoo's family. The Old Bag is coming with her 1000-year-old maid; the Gruesome Twosome are coming: so Cobra, her loser husband and children, and Psycho with her crack husband and tribe of children and a thousand bore-bore, ugly-ugly rellies whose names I now forget. Why? Because he's the son and the head of the family and it's his duty to gather all the members of his loser family under one roof at least once a year. That's why. Aagay-peechay when it comes to doing rishtas, vaghera, and standing for elections, nobody is giving him even this much of importance but when it comes to lena-dena and doing big-big expensive things, he becomes head of family.

Now look at Psycho, she's gone and done a rishta of her daughter with this very paindu but very rich family from Faisalabad, you know, the kinds who have fridges in the dining room and cases of mangoes under their beds? Well, apparently the savaal was done ages ago and the karas were also put on last year on her fat wrists, but they told us only when the engagement cards were being printed and pretended keh everything has been done bas, abhi-abhi. And look at The Old Bag, such a snake in grass she's turned out to be. She kept it from her own son since she knew that Janoo would object because he has soft spots for Nicky—or Nikki, as her name is, you know, 'small' in Punjabi—who he thinks should study more and become something. Well she *is* going to become something, I told Janoo—a big, fat, paindu Begum with fat gold karas on her wrists and a case of mangoes under her bed!

Well, Psycho was dropping hints left, right and centre that Janoo should have family ka dinner in his house and also invite Nikki's in-laws. And I bet they will want Janoo to shower gifts on boy and girl. And who do you think will pay for the gifts? Janoo, of course. Snatch crusts of bread from his own poor Kulchoo's mouth in order to feed gulab jamans and luddoos to nasty Nikki and her nouveau husband. Over my dead buddy.

But, one thing Mummy and Aunty Pussy have taught me. Never do open fighting. Instead do clever hidden fighting, like a gorilla. So this is what I did: I got Mulloo, who was going to Bangcok, to buy me two watches—fake gold ki Rolexes from the Sunday market but in nice-nice, real-real looking boxes, for ten dollars each. I told her they were for the servants.

Anyways, when she brought them, I showed them to Janoo and said, 'Look, I got these from Dubai on our last trip—from money I'd saved from household expanses. Nikki and her husband are going to come to our house for first time. We should give them something nice, na.'

January 2006

Bush vows to rally world against Iran
'Sleuth sayer' warns Butterfly

I was supposed to go to Karachi for Marry Add-a-Late ball for New Year. It happens every year, na. And I want to go every year but Janoo never wants to go, so I have no choice except to stay at home and eat Janoo's head for not taking me and then dragging him around to at least fifteen parties in revenge.

But this time Fluffy and Flopsy said, 'We know how much you want to go to Karachi and we also know how going alone looks desperate in a woman of your age, so you come with us. You can sit at our table.'

What do they mean, 'woman of your age'? Flopsy may have been one year behind me at school but only because she failed three years. And each year she failed and was kept back, her age also got one year less. Had she stayed at the Convent and continued failing every year, she would have been the only sixteen-year-old in nursery. But her luck changed when she failed for the fourth time. Her father was posted to Pindi and she went off there to Presentation Convent pretending to be seven when she was actually ten.

So first tau I wanted to tell Flopsy to go to hell, but then the thought of the ball made me swallow my pride. Ab dekho na, big things need big sacrifices. I mean, when Nehru offered Jinnah Pakistan without Kashmir, Jinnah also took, nahin? When I got home and asked Janoo, he said it was a splendid idea, the best suggestion he'd heard all year, and that I must go. In fact, he insisted I stay in Karachi for as long as I wanted.

'You mustn't rush back,' he said. 'Stay until Feb, March, if you like.'

'Haw, but won't you miss me?' I asked him.

'What? Miss you? Er, of course, of course. But we'll manage, Kulchoo and I. It will be hard but somehow or the other we'll find the strength to cope. Isn't that right, K?'

And Kulchoo, shweetoo, who was drinking a milkshake—I think so it was vanilla—nearly choked.

So immediately I said, 'No, no, I'll stay if it makes you upset.'

But Kulchoo, who was now cuffing and spluttering, shook his head a thousand times and the minute he got his voice back he said over and over again, 'No, no, please, you mustn't stay. Abba's right. Go, stay for a month, two, three months.'

Everything was ready. Table had been bought, air tickets booked, jora ironed, hair ironed, face ironed, no, no, I mean facial done—and then like a fool I decided at the last minute to go and consult Mummy's sleuth sayer. Mummy has one she's been going to in Model Town for years. She checks with her even before she goes to the bazaar. Her name is Baji Firdaus and she's never, ever wrong. She once told Mummy

160

to be aware of black. And that day, very same day, as Mummy was going to a big lunch at the Punjab Club with her hair all up in a big bee-hive, a crow swooped down and did big bathroom all over her lovely stiff bee-hive. Baji Firdaus even predicated Twin Towers. Imagine!

So anyways, you know, na, that I've never been a very good flyer in planes, so despite of myself, I asked. And you know what she said? 'What goes up must come down.' Or something like that.

Immediately I knew what she was talking about. So of course I didn't go. Only a fool would travel after such a clear warning of a crash. Janoo was very puzzled and sorry also. Kept asking why I'd changed my mind up and tried to get me to think again. Even offered to go drop me himself in Karachi. Of course I didn't tell him why I wasn't going because he'd have laughed till he cried. He doesn't believe, na. Because he's a septic. But I kept saying, 'Didn't feel up to it.' And Kulchoo, my little baby, tau looked actually so disappointed, so disappointed keh pooch hi na. So much he wanted his mother to have nice time. Dekho kitni meri care kartay hain, nahin?

February 2006

Danish newspaper publishes cartoons of Prophet Muhammad
Butterfly does Eid

Janoo and me always have this thug of war over Eid. He says we have to go and have Eid lunch with The Old Bag, and I insist that we <u>should</u> have it with Mummy and all. It's always a tossed up and the casting vote goes to Kulchoo.

'That's not fair!' I protest every year to Janoo, 'you know how mercury Kulchoo is.'

'Mercenary. The word's "mercenary". And I wonder where he gets it from?'

'How I should know?' I say with a shrug, as if I'm least bothered. 'Kulchoo'll opt for the place he gets the largest amount of Eidi and you know how The Ol... Ammi spoils him. Not like Mummy, who's strick because she knows the value of a good brought up.'

So it's always lunch at The Old Bag's and dinner, if we're lucky, at Mummy's. Kulchoo makes a fortune and I have to dish out to the Gruesome Twosome's nasty kids and all The Old Bag's servants and God knows who else. I tell you, Eid's no fun if you're at the giving end. I'd much rather just continue with

Ramzan—sehri, namaaz, sleep, namaaz, sleep, namaaz, sleep and then iftaar. So simple, so holy, so unfussy, so inexpensive.

Anyways, we arrived there and found the Gruesome Twosome and their tribe of baal bachas dressed in horrible durex joras. Or was it Lurex? Khair, whatever it was, it was very ugly and very last year. But you know me, na, always so polite, so dignified. So I didn't comment. Just gave the Gruesome Twosome one long look from head to toe and then, with a small-sa smile, went and sat in a corner and started sending text messages to Mulloo, Mummy and all, saying Eid Mubarak to everyone. But taubah, majaal hai if they would leave me alone for one minute. Janoo's family, that is.

First maid comes with juice. 'Please have,' she says.

'What juice is it?' I asked.

'Anaar,' she said.

'I hate anaar,' I said, jabbing the keys on my phone.

Then another maid comes with a plate of something greasy and shoves it under my nose. 'Have samosas,' she says.

'I'm doing Atkins,' I told her, pushing the disgusting plate away.

Then the bachas come and stand in front of me. 'Eid Mubarak, Maami,' they said, looking pointedly at my bag. Greedy jaisay. Honestly! So I opened my bag, opened my wallet and gave them a 100 each. They looked at me with dismay. Janoo had given me 1000 rupees kay notes for children's Eidi, but I kept those well hidden in the inside zipped-up department of my

163

bag. They're for other more deserving people, like Flopsy's nieces, whose parents have a huge compartment in London ka Knightsbridge where I will inshallah go and spend whole of summers next summers.

Then lunchtime came. Usual bore paindu food: aloo gosht, nargisi koftas, biryani, chicken qorma, chicken karahi, behari kebabs, shaami kebabs, seekh kebabs, pasandas, saag gosht, tawa fish, shabdeg, haleem, brain masala, keemay-waalay naan and siri payas, followed by shahi tukras, kheer, badaam ka halwa and some cake from somewhere. Ek tau The Old Bag's cook also knows nothing. Na koi pizza, na koi pasta, na koi cold slaw, na koi trifle.

Anyways, they kept insisting I eat, so I looked at the table and said, 'But what *is* there?'

Just then, thanks God my phone rang. It was Mummy. 'Yes, Mummy,' I said, sitting at the lunch table sandwiched between the Gruesome Twosome. 'I'm coming. As soon as I'm done from here. They're serving lunch so it won't be long now, hopefully. Haan, and please wait lunch for me. There's nothing here.'

On the way home Janoo wouldn't talk to me. He said I'd been rude and ungrateful. Dekho zara! *I'm* ungrateful? What about him, who never even thanked me for wasting half my afternoon on his precious rellies? Haan? Honestly, I tau have seen with my own eyes now. The more you do, the more taken for granted you get. Only good thing was, Kulchoo got given ten thou Eidi. Chalo, at least someone is happy.

March 2006

Manmohan offers peace treaty to Pakistan
Aunty Pussy and Mummy at war

Such a huge big phudda Mummy and Aunty Pussy have had. It was over Jonkers. At least I think so it was over Jonkers, but maybe it was about more. Maybe it was about them, the two of them. But outshot is that they aren't speaking and I don't think so they are ever going to speak. To each other, that is.

It all started when Aunty Pussy complained to Mummy that I wasn't maaroing enough hands and feet to help Jonkers find a new wife.

'All she cares about are her coffee parties and her lunches and her hairdresser and her tailor,' grumbled Aunty Pussy. 'So selfish she is, never thinks about introducing my poor old son to anyone worthwhile.'

'But only last week she took you to meet that girl,' said Mummy.

'Which girl?

'Bhai, the teacher. You know, that girl with the teeth.'

'*Girl?* You call that buck-toothed, grey-haired elderly person a *girl*?' shrieked Aunty Pussy. 'If those are the sorts of girls she is going to show Jonkers she might as well not bother. I mean, *really!*'

'She wasn't grey-haired,' protested Mummy. 'She had golden streaks.'

'Everyone knows girls put in golden streaks when they want to hide the silver streaks.'

'What do you mean?' demanded Mummy. 'My daughter has gold streaks.'

'Exactly!' said Aunty Pussy.

'And what about your son, ji?'

'My son doesn't have streaks.'

'Your son doesn't have any hair to put streaks in.'

'Are you saying Jonkers is losing his hair?'

'*Losing? Losing?* Has lost. Is bald. Is loser. Has two failed marriages behind him and a huge belly in front of him. How do you expect my daughter to find him decent rishtas?'

'Your daughter couldn't find a decent rishta even if it slapped her in the face.'

'Then why are you asking her, hain? Calling her thousand-thousand times a day and eating her head and drinking her blood.'

'Because I want to give her empty, boring life some meaning.'

'Empty? Boring? She has house, social life, money, servants, status, cars, jewellery. What more can anyone want? Oh, and she also has husband and child. I think so you are just jealous. You've always been jealous. Even in school you were jealous. I remember how you took out the eyes of my dolly that Daddy got from Bombay. Because I had dolly and you didn't. You've always been like that—jealous, sarrhial, mean and nasty.'

'Jealous of *you?* That's a joke. Married to a nobody, a servant in someone else's business. Doesn't even have his own factory,' sniffed Aunty Pussy.

'It's not an ordinary factory,' shrieked Mummy. 'It is a multinationalist with busy-busy factories in Jakarta and Africa and big-big offices in America and London. And he's an officer, not a servant, an officer with a tie and briefcase. Which your thief-tax collector-embezzler husband couldn't become even if he tried for a thousand years. And by the way, the tax collector's rishta came first for me and only when I turned it down, because he was too poor and bore and ugly, did his mother come for you. Second-hand.'

'Don't make me open my mouth, ji,' screamed Aunty Pussy. 'As if your upright husband with his briefcase and his tie hasn't been caught with the till in his paws, I mean, paws in the till. You've forgotten how he was almost thrown out by the big multi-nationalist company? Hain? And how his membership of Sindh Club was almost cancelled had it not been for my husband doing sifarish with the governor then, hain? Forgotten? Got almesia now, have you?'

'You know, you've always been petty and mean and I don't want to talk to you. Ever!' shouted Mummy.

'Same here!' shouted Aunty Pussy.

And they both slammed phones, and now I'm not looking for girl for Jonkers and Mummy's told me to turn my back on him if I see him at any dinner-shinner (not that he's ever invited to any), and to forget I ever had an aunt called Pussy.

So I'm not looking for girl for Jonkers. Till at least tomorrow, when Mummy and Aunty Pussy will make

April 2006

So much of fun these shaadis are, yaar. And thanks God the garmi is holding off a bit, which means keh I don't have to go dressed as a Hindu widow in white malmal. In fact, one shouldn't blow too hard on one's own drum, but I tau have gone as Ashwariya Rai in green contract lenses and green satin sari with blue sequences. Everyone said I looked splitting copy of her, Mummy, Aunty Pussy, and, er—Mummy and even Aunty Pussy, who doesn't do anyone's praise for free. I had agreed to take Jonkers along to spot nice-nice girls for prospectus wives.

Pehlay tau I went to Humair's wedding, na. Oho, baba, to Maha Rehman. Shaheema and Tariq Rehman's daughter, bhai. There was a qawwali at Shaheema's. Very tasteful, very nice.

Even Janoo, sarrhi boti, didn't complain for once. In fact, he's been singing Shaheema's praises. 'Instead of feeding the fat cats of Lahore, she's given the money she would have spent on the wedding to the earthquake victims. She's put her money where her mouth is.'

I wanted to tell him if he'd put his money in my account I'd also put my mouth there, but then I thought maybe silent is golden. He's in a good mood so rarely these days that there's no need to take panga for nothing. So I put one pathar on my dil and a bigger one around my neck (the emerald that The Old Bag gave me at our mangni—first and last nice thing she ever gave me) and went off to Meher Sethi's mehndi.

What a spread, yaar! What intezaam, what decoration (I think so professionals did it), what khaana, what peena! So big-hearted, so splashy. Main tau bilkull swept up ho gayee.

'Bas,' I said to Janoo, 'I tau will do a same-to-same mehndi for Kulchoo. No expense spared. You just wait and see, I will…'

'No. We'll do what Shaheema's done. We'll celebrate, of course, with a few close friends, but nothing lavish. We'll give the money away instead.'

Trust Janoo to pour water over all my plans. But I have also decided with myself that I'm not going to get into a you-you-me-me kind of phudda with him. Instead I will try to be all sweet si, understanding si, oopar-oopar se, but inside-inside I will do exactly what I want. Which is to have a HUUUUUGE wedding.

'Haan, bilkull theek hai, darling. So clever you are, so sober, so bo… I mean, committed,' I cooed. 'We'll have a quiet-si, choti-si wedding and we'll send money for hundreds of degs at Data Sahib, but for the mehndi we'll get J&S to do a Mittal-type function with Indian stars and elephants at a French chatto like Where Sigh, except that I'll request Jalal to make one right here in Gulberg only, in the empty plot by Mummy's house, and invite about a 1000 of my closest friends. That way, we'll give to charity also and get into *Good Times* also with Wedding of the Year and all your sober se, sedate se, bore se friends will also say keh bhai, so much of responsibility they've shown by giving so much away. And who knows, maybe we can even get into TFT with an article about our philan-trophy and perhaps even a profile of you. Kaisa???'

May 2006

London bombs linked to Al Qaeda: UK
Butterfly bites Cobra

I've just come, na, from Billoo's graduation in Boston. He went to some place called U-Mess. Did law-shaw or something like that. Billoo kaun hai? You may well ask. He's Janoo's nephew. Son of Janoo's older sister, Cobra, whom I hate less than only one other person in the world—her sister, Psycho. So why did I go? To keep an eye on Janoo, in case voh over ho jaye aur thousands of dollars ka graduation present na day de.

And just as well I went, because when Janoo gave me the lifafa to keep in my handbag that he was going to present to Billoo after his ceremony, I saw that it was bulging alarmingly. So I said excuse me and pretended I needed to go and do small bathroom. I nipped around the corner and carefully opened the envelope to find ten hundred dollar ke notes all crisp-crisp inside. I tau fauran took out five notes and shoved them into my bra. Then I thought, Janoo shouldn't get suspicious keh lifafa has become too thin. So I counted out five one-dollar ke notes and I slid them inside instead.

Janoo may have forgotten, but I remember that we have a son called Kulchoo: and soon we'll have to pay his college fees, and get him married, and build him an annexe to our house, and buy him his first car, and then his first house, and also pay for his servants, and his children's school fees, and khaana-peena and petrol, vaghera. And God knows how expensive petrol will be then. And anyways, meray se poocho tau 500 is also too much for Billoo. But if I took out more than that Cobra might report. This way she will think maybe Janoo gave only five hundred and five dollars and stay chup.

The risk was worth taking because as soon as bore graduation ceremony was over, I rushed to Maasi (sorry, sorry, Macy) in Boston and bought three pears of shoes—one silver, one gold and one silver-and-gold. Then I also got some MAC ki lipsticks and D&G ka sent and La Prarry ki face cream and Landcomb ka mascara, and it all came to so little that I felt sorry for myself and so shopped some more from Billoo's graduation money. I told Janoo keh honestly, shopping tau is best in America, and they are so wanting you to have a nice day that you can't possibly disappoint them, haina? Thanks God we didn't have to stay with Cobra in Boston for more than three days.

Vahan se we came straight to London, and uff, kuch na poocho, so much of garmi keh we tau thought we were going to pass out. Na koi AC na kuch. Honestly, so backward London is. Saw *Da Vinci's Coat*. Such a bore film. It's about some train or rail or something that's holy. Fazool...

June 2006

War erupts in Sri Lanka
Butterfly too hot to write

Got back to Lahore from Boston last week. Uff baba, it's so hot, so hot, keh don't even ask. Too hot to think, to talk, to write.

July 2006

Israel kills 60 in Lebanon massacre
Mulloo buys a Porsche

Ek tau Janoo is such an embarrassment also. So out of it he is. So untrendy, so dheela, so behind when it comes to knowing what's hot and what's not. Take Mulloo's party yesterday.

Talking of Mulloo, I'm sooooo jay of her and Bobby's new car. It's a bright red Porch. Mulloo looks a bit—vaisay kehna nahin chahiye, what with her being my best friend and all—but she looks so strange, so bazaar sitting in such a hot car with her hijab flapping in the wind. She tells me she's put a taaveez in the car, and also does duas and phookoes it every morning because people look with so much of envy at them when they come roaring out of their house—which is just beside the ganda nala with its rotten eggs and big-bathroom smells.

She tells me also that although she's constantly shooing them away when they have to stop at traffic lights, beggar children keep putting their dirty hands on the windows and Bobby's had to send for a special non-bleach glass-cleaning spray just for car from London only. They've also had a porch built for the Porch right in front of their sitting room where the old lawn used to be, so when they are entertaining all the guests can see the car—all gleaming and spot-lit and everything out of the big-big glass windows—with the big, gleaming swimming pool behind. I think so it's a bit shoda of them but then you know, na, that Mulloo didn't go to KC. She is a Home Econmics girl. So what can you expect?

Haan, so I was telling you about the dinner party. Janoo was banging on and on about mangoes and how much he loves Dussehris and Langras and some-thing else called Summer Bewitched or something. People there were looking so bored and I tau was just respiring—sorry, sorry, expiring—with embarrass-ment, na. So I said, with a light, tinkly si laugh, 'Mangoes are so over, Janoo.'

'What do you mean?' he asked. 'The season's very much on.'

'She doesn't mean over,' added Mulloo, laughing in a not-so-tinkly-way, 'she means OVER! As in unfashionable. As in bore. We tau just eat rambutan from Al-Fatah only, flown in fresh from Bangcock. Not so expensive. Just 800 rupees a kilo. So much nicer than mangoes, which I tau find so smelly, baba. And talking of smells, you know that motia that grows in your garden, darling,' she said, turning to me, 'so cute, I thought, it was. So quaint!'

'What's quaint about motia?' asked Janoo with that tight-lipped look of his he gets when he's just about to explode. 'For me it signifies summer.'

'How sweet,' Mulloo murmured. 'Depends where you spend your summers. For us tau summers are just orchids.'

'Tell me, Mulloo,' I said finally, 'when are you going to learn to swim? After all, you've had your pool for what, five years now?'

August 2006

Akbar Bugti killed in army action
Butterfly's air conditioner mysteriously stops

Uff, it's so hot, so hot, I tau swear Janoo's brain has melted. Bechara, crack tau he always was but now he's gone and got start staring mad. Such strange-strange things he's started doing. Pehlay tau he went and sold the Suzuki on which I sent the cook to buy sauda, saying we didn't need four-four cars and that it was polluting the air needlessly. Then he started switching off lights in empty rooms. And now he refuses to let me have my bedroom ka AC on when I'm not there. Imagine! In this heat! Can you think of a bigger zulm? First I thought it must be tripping. The AC, not Janoo.

I'd just come back from lunch at Mummy's and when I entered my room, I got such a blast of Saharan heat that I nearly got knocked up. So first I called the servants and screamed at them, but they said they didn't know anything, and then I called Shareef the electrician, who is badmash number one, it turns out. He hummed and hawed over it and said maybe it's the coolant, maybe the heatant, maybe the oppressor (or was it compressor?) or maybe just the dictator. Anyways, he charged me a thou but he got it going.

When Janoo came home I told him what had happened and first his face turned purple, then maroon, then red. Then he said, 'Did you not bother to have a look at that infernal machine yourself?'

'In case you haven't noticed, I'm not an electrician or a mechanic or something, achha?'

'Had you looked, even you, with your limited intelligence, would have realised that it was merely switched off.'

'*Switched off?*' I shrieked. 'You know I only switch it off in October.'

'Well, I did it today,' said Janoo. And then he started saying such weird-weird things that I tau nearly went behosh. Apparently, at least according to Janoo, there is someone called Paula who has an ice-cap which has melted. Now if you will wear ice caps in summers, what do you expect, hein? And then they say we desis have silly fashions! Then he started ranting about some Global Warning that I think so someone has given. Must be Americans only. One day they are giving warning to Saddam, next day to Osama, then to Iran and now to that His Mullah or someone. And then on top he said there was climate change and that my sauday-wali Suzuki and my AC-until-October-habit were to blame. Suno zara! As if I'm, God forbid, God or someone who can change climates.

But Mummy always told me that when men go mad, always look as if you agree with them and then go and do just the opposite. So I said yes, I know it's all my fault, but if you don't mind I'd like to change the climate in my room to winters, and so saying I turned my AC onto terminal cool.

September 2006

**Musharraf and Manmohan agree to resume peace talks
Janoo sinks into depression**

Thanks God summers are over, well almost, and season has started, well almost. First there was that nice Munir (bhai, Structure-wallay nahin hain?) and Bilal wedding in Lahore. I tau went on all seven days. So much of fun. And bride's jora was tabahi—all 60 yards of it. Then there was Ali and Gillo Afridi's son's shaadi in Isloo. Too, too fantastic with all that rang-bhang being flung all over the place and all the planes-loads of Karachiites all black and blue. Just like Holly in Indian films. I tau pretended I was Pretty Zinta. Pity there was no Shahrukh, but chalo, maybe in my next life! At least look forward tau kar sakti hoon, na.

Gillo and Ali have been living in Dubai forever. Actually even before forever—from olden days when Dubai-wallahs used to come for shopping to Karachi—Imagine! Someone was saying that Gillo is tau like an institution of Dubai. I think so she must be a bit like the Eye-full Tower in Rome.

Janoo of course didn't go to a single day of a single shaadi. He is still in morning for Akbar Bugti, oho, baba, the head of the Bugti tribe, whom the army killed, na, and then pretended he'd died himself only. He wouldn't listen to them, na, and had taken refuse in a cave in the dessert. So they came after him with helicopters and bombs and things, and then they said his cave had fallen down on him in Balochistan and he'd died of natural becauses. Apparently not just the Bugtis, but all of Balochistan is up in arms against Musharraf now.

But what's to Janoo, haan? He's not even Balochi, let alone a Bugti. I said so to him that day and uff, you should have seen how he drew off the handles!

'It's not just Bugti I'm mourning,' he shouted, 'it's my country. You can go and dance your feet off if you want, but with Balochistan in flames I can't find all that much to celebrate.'

'Haw, tau what's happened to the fire engines, baba?' I asked. 'Why can't they put out the flames in your precious Balochistan?'

Bas. That's all I said, and he tau almost went up in flames himself. Just like Twin Towers. I think so he is depress. All he talks of is Afghanistan and His Mullah and Gaza and someone else called Helmand, and how the Bugtis—man, woman, child—are on the Exist Control List, and Global Warning and God knows what else.

I swear, I should get a medal the size of a frying pan for putting up with him without going start staring mad. Aunty Pussy tau says I should get Nishan-e-Haider. But Mummy says no, I deserve the Noble Prize for Piece. Like Nelson Mandela and Mother Theresa and Shirin Mahal—or was it Abadi? Anyways, you know who I mean, baba. That Egyptian, or was

October 2006

North Korea tests nuclear bomb
Butterfly placates God

Thank God, Ramzan will finish before proper party season starts. Varna tau all the weddings, all the parties, everything would have had water poured over them. Haw, maybe I shouldn't have said that. Everyone is saying the Muslim God is wrathful. What if I'm stuck down now? Hai, please, Allah Mian, sorry, sorry, didn't mean that, na. Please don't take personally, okay? I mean, if it wasn't for this nice month-long rest when would I get the time to get my party wardrope sorted, hain? And my manicure and pedicure done? And my highlights put? And just to show You how sorry I am, I'm going to have a nice big iftaar in Your name only. I hope You are going to give me lots of savaabs for opening fast of so many people. Or were they supposed to be poor people whose fast you have to open to get credit points in the afterlife?

But what to do: I don't know any poor people. At least not since I discovered that Janoo's cousin Shameless (well, her real name's Shama), who I used to take pity on because her husband's hardwear shop had gone thup and who I used to think was hand-to-mouth and who I used to give all my last-season designer joras to, turned out to have won some huge lottery in Toronto and was the proud owner of not one, not two, but three compartments in Toronto— and that too in the best bit of town, somewhere called Missy Saga, which is like Gulberg of Toronto. Anyways, with that snake in grass Shameless a millionaire I don't know any more poor people. But I suppose if all my guests bring their drivers then I could open their fasts and get all my savaabs, couldn't I? So now I must make sure no one drives their own car.

I'll have to tell Tony bhai not to bring his Porch in that case. He tau won't even let his driver put his little finger on it, except to clean, of course. And also I'll have to manao Janoo before I can do iftaar parties. He hates them, you know, iftaar parties. He says it's just an orgy of eating and self-righteous opining and he's had it with self-righteous opining after reading Mush's new thriller, *In the Land of Fire*.

He thinks Mush has gone too far and bus, it's only a matter of time now before the Americans organise a little plane crash for him too. Hai, please don't speak like that, I said to Janoo, at least let me have my iftaar party before we all go up in flames.

In any case, I really don't know why Janoo is after Mush the whole time. He's given us so many TV channels and pop groups and so many fashion shows and so many of mobile phones, we should get down on our feet and thank him. Has any democrat ever given this much? Hain? And so what if he's not elected? Did I elect The Old Bag to be my mother-in-law? Sometimes you just have greatness thrust upon you, and then you just have to grin and bear it. So I'm grinning and Janoo's bearing.

November 2006

Mark Lyall-Grant is going, na. Bhai, the British Deputy Commissioner. So lots of bye-bye parties are happening in Isloo, Karachi and here. I wanted to take my passport to the one here so that jaate-jaate he could give me five year multiple entry visa to London, so I don't have to gravel in Isloo till at least 2010. But Janoo said I was crack. One tau he doesn't give visas. Then who gives, I asked? The consular people, he said.

'Haw, the local council? Now *they* are giving? Must have khilaowed-pilaowed to get the stamp from British Deputy Commission.'

Janoo looked heavenward and shoved me into the car. So badtameez, he is. No manners, no proper utna-betna, no good brought-up. But what can you expect with The Old Bag for a mother? Not like my Mummy, who always taught me to keep my little finger up in the air when holding a teacup and always flushing first before sitting on toilet in other people's homes so they can't hear you actually doing small bathroom.

'Do you know Lyall-Grant's father founded Lyallpur?' Janoo asked me on the way to the party.

'Really?' I said, twisting the rearview mirror to my side to check my Channel ki new Rouge Noir lipstick.

'When did it get lost?'

Janoo heaved another sigh and snatched the rearview mirror back to his side. As I said, no brought-up he has.

December 2006

Law to be amended to easily dissolve forced marriages
Butterfly goes for gold

Hai, can't wait for shaadi season to start! Have ordered two joras from Kami—oho, baba, voh nahin hai designer, Kamra, sorry, sorry, Karma-wallah, okay?—two from Sonia Batla and one from Hasan Sheheryar, and I'll kill you if you tell Janoo. Vaisay it's not as if it's any of his business because I've not touched a penny of his. Kulchoo had them made for me.

Ji haan, Kulchoo! Why? Because he loves me and wants to see me happy. At least that's what he wrote in his school essay, 'I want my Mummy and Daddy to be happy.' So I thought, then he won't mind if I sell the gold ten-tolay ki brick that The Old Bag gave him for his last birthday. Anyways, what's he going to do with a ten-tola brick, hain? Whereas I, I could get a Hasan Sheheryar, a Karma, a Batla and live happily ever after—at least till the end of the month.

I think so I'll wear the Karma jora to one day in Sanam Taseer's wedding. I hear it's going to be a tabahi celebration over a whole week, with party and disco and dholak and mehndi and dinner, and then all of it all over again in the pages of *Good Times* to gloat over. Uff, so much of fun!! Janoo says I've become a fixture in *Good Times*. Vaisay to be honest I've started recognising their phot-graapher, na, and any time I spot him at a party or gallery opening or shaadi or whatever, I immediately pout and make sure I am standing inside his camera ki lens. Bhai, bus, one has to paddle one's own canoe in life otherwise who else is going to do it for you?

But I hope it won't go and rain, yaar, and spoil everything. That will be so bore. It's good it's happened now only—rain, bhai, what else? I think so some bits of Karachi and Lahore even have become so flooded that people have been macarooned in their houses. But I think so only in poor, poor bits of the city. Defence, Gulberg and GOR mein tau, mashallah, mashallah, everyone is warm and dry and party-ing away.

Talking of Karachi, I hear Shobha Day came there to launch a new novel by Nadia AR. It's called *Kolachi Nights* and so juicy it is with all the things I love most—goss and clothes and parties, vaghera. Maybe I should write one myself. I'll call it *Lahori Nights*—or no, *Lahori Days*. Bhai, one should be original, nahin, otherwise all those jealous types like Mulloo, Flopsy, vaghera say I've stolen the idea from someone else. As if I'm some copy cat or cheater cock or something.

January 2007

Saddam hanged
Janoo goes missing

Just look at Janoo! For the last four days there's been no naam or nishaan of him anywhere. I've been worrying myself to death—well, in between hurrying from one shaadi to another—wondering where he's disappeared to. I even sent the driver to the airport to check if he was coming off the Haj flight or something—you never know with him, na, he's forever sneaking off here and there. But it turns out that janaabji has been lurking all this time in Sharkpur! And with my son, Kulchoo, in toe. Father and son decided to bunk the wedding season and go off to—what does Janoo call it?—haan, 'presume with nature'. Or was it commune? Khair, whatever! It's just a show-off way of saying that he's a loser who wanders through muddy fields and drinks enormous steel ke glass, beloved of all paindus, full of smelly bufallow milk. (Thanks God for Nestlay ka milk, yaar. No more stinky cows for me.)

Anyways, going back to Janoo, I could have marroed some show about him, about how he's manly and bloodthirsty, if he'd had the grace to do at least some shikaar. But no! Voh bhi nahin! Wildlife, he says, is on the verge of distinction and the only shooting he'll do is with a camera. As if he's Mahesh Bhatt or something! All Kulchoo could talk about was having seen a nilgai in the wild. Honestly! Khud tau Janoo is what he is, but he's also gone and made my poor old son into a bucket case! And so black also, from wandering outside all day.

'Well,' I responded, 'I may not be one of your precious nilgais, but it may interest you to know that I was also on the verge of distinction worrying about you. At least you could have told me.'

'But, Mama,' said Kulchoo, 'we made the plan on the spur of the moment when you were at the hairdresser's. We called your mobile but you probably couldn't hear over the blowdryer. I even left a message but you never called back so I thought you were okay with our trip.'

Hmm. I remember dimly seeing a missed call from Janoo but since I knew it was going to be some bore complaint or the other, I never checked. But of course I couldn't admit that, so I started screaming and shouting about how the message never came and then Janoo said he'd show me his mobile to show the exact time and date when Kulchoo had made the call. And so I shouted even louder about how no one trusts me and no one cares how I feel, and how embarrassed I was having to lie to Naz and Mansha about how Janoo was ill in bed and so couldn't attend Hassan's fab valeema, and how I'd had to hitch a ride with Mulloo to Naila Moltifoams' New Year party like some poor bechari, and how I'm getting late for Bunny and Sarmad's valeema now and don't have the time to stand around arguing with two bucket case losers anyway...

190

February 2007

Palestinians sign unity government deal
Butterfly prepares for Basant parties

God is on my side. I've always known, but now it's official. If he hadn't been, then he wouldn't have ended Muharram in time for Basant, now would he? So all the mullahs and sarrhi botis can go fly a kite. Oh, sorry, forgot! They can't fly a kite because they believe it's anti-Islamic. Their nikahs will break, or some such thing, if they do so much as look at a patang. Well, they can go and do whatever it is that they do, because I tau damn care, frankly speaking.

So in keeping with Basant theme, I'm all ready with my sunflower-gold jora. Last year I had lemon-yellow one and the year before that butter yellow and the year before that a sort of jaundice yellow and the year before that mustard and the year before that—I've forgotten. Anyways, point is one should keep changing, na, otherwise people think you are struck in a grove and they start taking you for granted and aik dafa aap ko log for granted take karna shuroo ho jayen, tau bus, might as well give up then. So this time, knowing that surprise is best element of attack, I've also had my hair dyed a sort of sunflower yellow to keep up the surprise elements.

Now I'm all set for Basant. Let the count down begin...

March 2007

**Chief Justice Iftikhar Chaudhry suspended
Butterfly rages over shortened Basant**

Two days. Just two measly days of hulla-gulla, shor-sharaba, mill-jull. And then bus, thup! Everything finish, everything over. Khattam shud. Shutters down. Lights out. So unfair. So selfish. So spoil spot. So rondoo. Who? The fundos, baba, who else?

They went and shortened Basant to two days. Can you imagine? It comes after a whole year and then we can only celebrate for two days. And why? Because it is un-Islamic. Well, what else is Islamic then, hain? Cricket? Hockey? Did they used to play that back then? Bedminton? Football? And what about riding in cars and planes? The mullahs should ride on camels, then. And rocket launchers? And cruise missiles? Did they use that for doing jihad back then? No, they had arrows and swords. So let them fight the Americans with arrows and swords in Afghanistan. Why do they use bombs, hain? Bloody hypocrites, liars. I tau tell you, am so fed up. So up to here with their constant lectures and sermons. The minute they see someone having a bit of fun they come down on them like a cruise missile. Reminds me of Kulchoo's monopoly: 'Go to jail, go directly to jail. Do not pass Go. Do not collect 200 pounds.' Killed joys. Sarrhials. Bores. Losers.

But one good thing the beardos have done. They've brought Janoo and me together. Yes, promise by God. They've done the impossible. This is what happened: I came back from the second day's parties—you know Izzat Majeed's do at his farm and Asif Jah's haveli function and, of course, a quick hello-hi at Yusuf's and Bali's farm thing at Bedian, where incidentally Mush also came—and came home and wrenched my yellow stilettos off and hurled them across the room.

Janoo, who as usual was sitting reading some bore book, looked up mildly and said, 'Anything the matter?'

So I started abusing the fundos, of course. At this he put his book down, crossed his arms across his chest and said, 'Do I see the stirrings of a political consciousness here?'

'I don't know what you see, but I can tell you how I feel. FED UP. Itni fed up, keh bas pooch hi na. I mean, why can't the beardos go off to some island like Green Land or Blue Land or something and make their own bore kingdom for themselves, where no one is allowed to laugh or fly a kite or sing a song or wear sleeveless?'

'Might be a bit nippy to go sleeveless in Greenland. Global warming notwithstanding,' he murmured.

'What? Who's without standing? What are you talking about?'

'Nothing,' he said hurriedly. 'Go on.'

'Haan, why can't they just go off and leave us alone to sarrho, pay for our own sins and to answer Allah ourselves? It's not as if I'm asking anyone else to jump

193

into the fires of hell for me, am I? So why can't they leave us alone?'

At this he looked at me in wonder and said, 'Madam, I salute you!' And then he took me out to dinner. At Cosa Nostra. Candle light. Roses. Bliss.

April 2007

Countrywide protests for Chief Justice
No Thai soup for Butterfly

So much of trouble poor Gen Mush is in. And why? Because he threw out a judge. Big bloody deal, yaar. People throw their husbands and wives out and nobody turns a hare, tau what's all this fuss for a judge, hain? I tau think it's very unfair the way they are taking out jalooses and doing hartaals and being so mean to poor old Mush.

Quite apart from the fact that I haven't been able to go down the Mall for a little bit of Thigh food at Royal Elephant—that soup of theirs, Sum Yung Guy, is sooo delish—because of the jalooses that these spoil spot lawyers are taking out, I really think that they should have a little bit of lehaaz for a man who's allowed us fashion shows and satter-light TV and New Year's Eve parties. I mean it's not like he was like General Zia or something, who wouldn't let us wear sleeveless and dance at New Year's, haina? Honestly, Mush tau is my favourite general. So nice he is. You should ask the Indians, so jealous they are of us for having him. And that nice Shock Aziz with his nice, smooth-si voice and his nice, smooth-se manners and his nice, smooth-si sherwani. Honestly, that's our problem, never do enough Allah ka shukars.

As usual, I had a big fight with Janoo about it. Yes, I can hear you say, what's new? What's new is that we hadn't fought for a while. Part of the reason is that he was in Sharkpur for ten days—so he wasn't there to fight with—but part of the reason was also that we were not talking since our last fight. But anyways, we had a big fight over Mush and cricket.

Janoo, of course, is behaving as if the sacked judge was his own chacha and is taking it all very personally, and when I said, 'So what's the big deal?', I thought he was going to have a heart attack like poor old Bob Woolmer. And he said if our team played with even half the commitment with which they pray, then maybe we could win ten World Cups. And I said that he was just sarrhoing because he'd bought a new wall-mounted TV for the World Cup and now he has to watch Australia win in double size.

Actually, poor old Mulloo and Tony had booked tickets and made hotel reservations and everything for World Cup, and had been maaroing show for the last three months about how they were off in the first week of April to Carib Iranian. And now they have gone all quiet and the goss is that they are trying to get their money back and can't. Serves them right for being so shoda!

Anyways, I said to Janoo, why didn't he buy a book or something and read it to forget his sorrows about cricket and Bob Woolmer. And he said it was rich coming from me, considering I couldn't name a single book if he asked me. So I said, what nonsense he was talking.

And he said, 'Go on, then, name one book you know well.'

And cool as a cucumber, I said, 'Cheque book!' Kaisa?

May 2007

**Lal Masjid students kidnap foreigners, threaten mass
  suicide bombs
Butterfly participates in anti-extremism rally**

I went. Janoo went. Kulchoo went. So did Mummy,
Daddy, Aunty Pussy, Fluffy and Mulloo-Tony. Even
Jonkers went. Where? Uff, taubah! Where are you?
To the anti-fundo rally, of course. On April 14th in
Lahore. Everyone I know went. Yes, yes, I know, I'm
not the jaloosiya types and yes, I know you think I
did it only for shughal and getting my pictures in
papers, but you can think whatever you want, because
I damn care. I know why I went, and that's all that
matters. So why I went?

I went because enough is enough, baba. For the last
twenty years, ever since bloody Zia, I've been turning
a blind cheek and the other eye. Chalo, I thought, if
the fundos want to grow beards and carry Kalashnikovs
and wear their shalwars to show off their hairy
ankles, and put their women in burqas and their
sons in madrassahs, tau let them. Mera kya jaata
hai? They want to go and fight in Kashmir, tau let
them. They want to die in Afghanistan, tau let them.
Live and let live—or in this case, die—I thought.

But it's not like that. Because the fundos are not prepared to live and let us live. They tau are control freaks, yaar. Like class monitors, they want to tell us when we can talk and when we can't. When we can go to toilet and when we can't. When we can sit down and when we can't. Today they are saying that I can't wear sleeveless and must wear dupatta on my head. Tomorrow they will say I must wear chaadar. The day after they will say I must cover my face. Then they will say that even behind my niqab I can't wear make-up. Then they will say I can't even wear lipstick at home, or cut my hair, or wear sent, or paint my nails. Then they will say I can't drive. And nor can I sit in a car alone with a driver to whom I am not related by blood. Then they will say I can't go in mixed company. So I can't go to Al-Fatah to do my shopping, or go to Dynasty Chinese, or even to Tariq Amin's for my highlights and facial.

Parties tau will be completely out. Not even GTs will be allowed, so you can forget balls. Also going to London, Dubai, Singapore, vaghera, will be band. Then they will say I can't read English books or watch movies or listen to songs. Not even *Saas Bhi Kabhi Bahu Thi*. Then they will say I can't inherit property. So Daddy's house and all his shares vaghera will go to his brother's sons and all I'll inherit from him will be his blood pressure and diabetes. Then they will say Janoo can marry however many times he wants, and I can't say no to him. Then they will say I can't divorce him. And if I don't do as they say, then they will say that I am asking for it, and they will march me to a stadium and, in front of thousands of other beardo control freaks they will behead me. So you

June 2007

Stalemate over Lal Masjid
Butterfly leaves for London

Mulloo came to my house on the day before I was leaving for London—packing-shacking, everything was done—and said, 'Haw, are you crack or something, going to London?'

'Why?' I asked. 'Why am I crack?'

'Uff, taubah, so much of garmi there and no ACs and no pankhas even. So behind they are, na. We tau went last year and did taubah after. This year tau we are going to Thailand, where everything, even the swimming pool, is AC'd. My tau shoe even wouldn't go to London in summers. Not even if you paid it, baba.'

But thanks God, I didn't listen to Mulloo. Such a sarrhi boti she is. Tony is in trouble with the banks, na. They are calling in their loans and Tony is playing hide and seek all over the place with them. The Porch is gone and so is the second Prado. And last week I saw Mulloo's diamond earrings—the three-three-carrot-wallay drops—at Goldsmith's. She pretended they'd come to be fixed but Iqbal Sahib told me himself only that she's asking sixty Ls for them and 'not an anna less'. So I think so they can't afford

London and becharas, they are having to make do with Phookit. Maybe they can't even cuff up the 25 thou for the British ka visa.

But we can, and it's so nice here. So cool-cool, so breezy-breezy. A bit of rain, but Janoo keeps complaining and grumbling that he can't see Wimbledong but I tau damn care. Vaisay I think so the monsoon has come here also. In their Northern Areas tau there has been theek-thaak flooding-shlooding. Places like Badford and Leads and pata nahin kya. Where their Taliban types live. You know, the ninjas in their burqas and trainers and the mullahs with their beards down to their knees, who say, 'khuda hafiz, innit?' Them only.

But why spoil my holidays by thinking about all of that bore stuff? Particularly when so many nice, khaata-peeta types are here these days. At Deutsche Bank ki rich desis party last week there were Naseem and Sehyr Saigol, Saira Lakhani, Qadir Jaffer, Gillo Afridi, and also I hear Habib Fida Ali is here and Mian Sheheryar also, and Meliha and Sikander are coming and Monty and Amina have just gone and Popity is coming and so are Irfan and Gullie. Hai, so much fun, just like a huge desi GT in London. And poor Mulloo is sitting all by herself in boring old Phookit... Ya kismat ya naseeb.

July 2007

**Lal Masjid sacked by troops, dozens killed; mass
violence in Karachi
Jonkers has a narrow escape**

Look at MQM! Look at Musharraf! Look at the
army! Look at all these stuppid district councillors
who pushed their poors into buses and dragged them
all to Isloo for Musharraf's tit-for-tat jaloos with the
lawyers and judges. Shame on them! Stuppids! Not
the poors, the councillors. Honestly, hud hoti hai of
shamelessness. It's like Mulloo inviting me to tea and
then expecting me to bring my servants to serve. And
bringing all the chai ka samaan on top. And me going
along doing yai, yai like a besharam and taking them
all along in a trailer holding samosas and cakes.

Talking of Islamabad, I heard on Al Jazeera last
night keh government has finally seedha karroed the
Lal Masjid crazies. But why be all lovey-dovey and
'Ji huzoor, no problem, burn as many video shops as
you like' with them in the first place, then? Why
promise to rebuild their mosques and let them treat
that public library in Islamabad like their own sitting-
dining, then? Janoo says Mush has lost the plot.
Which one, I said? A four-star general like Mush tau
gets so many. And not just residential plots but

agricultural lands also. In Sharkpur all of the biggest zamindars are now generals.

I tell you, the CJM (no, no, that's Convent of Jesus and Mary), the CJS (haan, I remember, it stands for Chief Justice of Supreme Court, but then why isn't there another C at the end?), haan, I was saying the CJS is my new hero. Shame he doesn't look more like Brad Pitts, but he's still my hero. Janoo tau is one minute up, one minute down, just like the mouse in the clock. Pehlay he was so excited, so excited keh poocho hi na. He kept banging on about the re-assessment, or was it reassertion, anyways something important of civil society. He took part in every single jaloos, every single protest in Lahore, and wrote hundred-hundred letters to the newspapers on top, asking for chief justice to be reinstalled. But now he says lawyers are beginning to act like a political party. They are electioneering instead of lawyering.

'Just make up your mind,' I said, 'instead of running up and down the clock.'

He looked at me as if I'd gone mad. I think so he didn't understand my illusion to the mouse in the clock. Poor thing, he is not poetry-minded like me.

But it was poor Jonkers, really, who got it in the neck. He was in Karachi that day, na, when CJS was expected to give speech there in big jaloos but wasn't allowed to step into the city by MQM. That's when MQM went off on that killing spree. (Janoo should give a thousand thanks that I only do shopping sprees.) Haan, so what was I saying? Yes, Jonkers in Karachi: Aunty Pussy has a plot just on the backside of Drigh Road and she'd sent him to find buyers for it. So anyways, you know that Jonkers never reads the papers and on TV also he only watches the film channel, so he didn't know CJS was expected in Karachi. So he arrived at the plot where he had appointment with a state agent and he waited and waited but no one came. He said the streets were a bit quietish and a bit emptyish and also a bit spookyish and he started feeling a bit worried-sa.

For a moment or two he even considered going home but then the thought of Aunty Pussy's ghussa was even more scary, so he stood and stood but still the state agent wouldn't come, wouldn't come. Finally he saw a motorbike coming slowly towards him, and he was so reliefed to see someone at last that he was about to run and throw his arms around them, but as the motorbike got closer he saw there were two men and one had the lower half of his face covered by a handkerchief, like, you know, thiefs and murderers in cowboy films, and the other was carrying a Kalashnikov and looking as bloodthirsty as Dracula, honest by God.

Jonkers tau poor thing was so terrified that he dived into the bushes of his old house and sat there hunched up, shivering and shaking like Aunty Pussy's upper arms. Luckily the motorcycle-wallahs didn't see him. But he saw everything. All the khoon-kharaba and the murders and the firing and the killing that took place on that street that day. And the police standing to one side, picking their noses. He was there in the bush for nine hours, poor Jonkers. Itna trauma hua hai becharay ko keh poocho hi na. So shame on Musharraf, shame on MQM, shame on all the stuppids who did this to bechara Jonkers. And, oh yes, I must remember the poors who died also.

August 2007

Musharraf and Benazir in secret talks in Dubai
Bob Woolmer's death from natural causes: Butterfly

So sad. So, so, so sad. Such high hopes I had of Mush.
In fact, everyone had. Mulloo, Tony, Aunty Pussy,
Mummy, Fluffy, even Jonkers, who, bechara, after
all his broken marriages had stopped being hopeful
altogether. And now Mush has gone and bashed
all our hopes. We never thought he'd go conkers
like this.

Only Janoo, sarrhi boti, in his usual doom and
bloom way, always said, 'Mark my words, however
much he might bang on about enlightened modera-
tion and however liberal and open he might seem, a
general is in the end a general. He doesn't know how
to share power.'

Such poocho tau, I tau damn care about power
shearing, as long as he keeps us happy and rich. House
prices were rising (ours is for ten crores now,
mashallah), international supermarkets were coming,
Americans were happy with us, olive oil was flowing
in Al-Fatah, and after all these years, shopping in
Delhi's Khan Market had become so easy. What more
does anyone want, haan? Okay, I admit, there were
a couple of little things, like that Red Mosque phudda

where he let the chicks with sticks hold all of Isloo to handsome for weeks and weeks before blasting them off the face of the earth, and then there was the punga he took with the Just Chieftess, but really, these are such choti-choti things when you compare them to the big-big things like house prices vaghera, that I tau feel that we should forgive and forget.

I said to Janoo when he was going on and on about Mush, 'Just look how much of freedom Mush gave to the press! *Good Times, Begum Nawazish Ali, Zainab Can't Cook, Sunday...*'

'The army must learn to let go,' he said. 'Musharraf is stifling civil society. And it won't work. It just won't work.'

'Maybe it's the heat,' I said. 'If ACs are melting, maybe his brain is also melting.'

'His political system is certainly in meltdown,' said Janoo.

God knows who will come now. Benazir or Nawaz? I am tau so sick of that silly ping-pong. They come, they loot, they go. One is sitting in big, fat flat in London and the other is sitting in big, fat flat in Dubai and talking from there only about what-what they will do, and how horrid Mush is and how lovely they are! And here we are all sarrhoing in the heat with loadshedding on top.

But one piece of khush khabri. Now goras are saying Bob Woolmer died himself only and that nobody killed him. Dekho zara. After all those suspicious looks at our poor, namaazi, God-fearing players, and all that talk of match-fixing and poisoning and doing DMA testing of them and muttering-shuttering about bribery and corruption. Just because

September 2007

Benazir returning to Pakistan on 18 October
Flopsy gets nose job

Goss is—and not just aissee-vaissee, everyday goss, but real, reliable goss—that Mush was about to declare emergency but Condi Rice called in the middle of night and told him, 'Khabardaar!'

Apparently his finger was two inches away from emergency button when phone rang. 'Hello? Kaun?' he said.

'It's me only. Miss Condiment Rice. Listen, I'm telling to you keh bilkull don't even think about it. Varna no one will be worse than us. And then don't say we didn't say. Okay? Now take your finger out and go to sleep. And when you wake up in the morning go and hunt Talibans.'

And phone went 'kharrack' after that.

But problem is, what is Mush to do? Janoo says Americans are saying, 'Go fetch Benazir Bhutto', but BB is also not maanoing. As Janoo says, she's no Sonia Gandhi willing to stay in the background and let someone from her party become PM. Na, ji, na, not in a thousand, million years. She'd rather put her dog on the PM's chair than any of her party members. Did you see the way she became so jay of Aitzaz when he was all over the papers for fighting with Mush over chief justice? Janoo tau thought she was going to throw him out on his ear then and there only. Also, if she doesn't become PM then how is she going to make more money? Sochnay ki baat hai, vaisay. So God alone knows who's going to come.

Bhai, I tau want anyone but mullahs. Even Imran or Nawaz are better, but Janoo says that they are hand-in-glove with mullahs. And because they like to pretend they are not, they are much more dangerous.

Matric results have come. Our driver's son got second division pass. He was eating Janoo's head to get him sarkari naukri. Janoo did some sting-pulling and got him into Forests, but he says he wants Customs or Police and not a bonga job with no money-making prospectus like Forests. Janoo's told him to go to hell.

Mulloo's back from Singapore with a suitcase full of shoes and bags. Flopsy's come back from New York with a new nose. She swears she's had nothing done, but in June her nose was a jacket potato and now it's a french fry. Jhoothi jaisi. Honestly, so full of liars and cheaters this country is. No wonder we are an emergency...

October 2007

Suicide bomber targets Benazir
Butterfly queries Mulloo's hair colour

Look at them! Bursting bombs on Benazir's jaloos and killing so many peoples. You know yesterday I was watching TV late into the night because Janoo tau, you know, he is a news ka junkie, na, and he wouldn't switch off the wall-mounted 48-inch ka screen in our bedroom which he got for World Cup, even though it was so late at night. And so I was also forced to watch, and one minute it was claps and cheers and dhols and dhoom and the next, smoke and screams and dhamaakas and bodies. Next day, jab pata chala it was suicide bomb tau Janoo immediately announced that it was Al Qaeda.

'Hai, bhai, how you can be sure?' I asked.

'Because only ideological zealots blow themselves up,' he replied.

I wanted to ask him who is Zealot, but you know he makes such sarrhial faces when you ask him any questions keh I thought, keh kyoon apnay aap ki besti karaani, hain? And anyways silent is golden.

Anyways, next day we went to Mulloo's for dinner and Janoo was saying what a relief it was that Benazir didn't get harmed, when Tony said: 'Haan, khud tau she survived and got so many innocent people killed. I tau think she has blood on her hands.'

'What?' Janoo asked, open-mouthed.

Oh God, I thought, now there is going to be tu-tu-main-main. So quickly I said to Mulloo, 'Hai, Mulloo, your hair is looking so nice, phir se dye karae hain?'

'What do you mean, "blood on her hands"?' asked Janoo in that soft-si voice he puts on just before he explodes.

'Ji nahin,' snapped Mulloo. 'My hair is naturally auburn.'

'So many times Musharraf had said, "Don't do jalooses, don't do jalooses,"' said Tony. 'Instead, go in helicopter. We know the risks, baba, because we know everything. But would she listen? Never! Ziddi to the last, just like her father.'

'If they knew the risks, why didn't they give her better security?' asked Janoo.

'It must be the light, then, Mulloo,' I continued desperately, 'because honestly your hair is looking almost carrot-coloured.'

'Problem is,' said Tony, leaning back in his leather armchair and resting his huge glass of whisky on his paunch, 'these rich, corrupt politicians, what do they care about the poor man on the street. Hain, ji? All they care about is votes. What does it matter to Benazir if three hundred, even three thousand die? Unlike us, politicians don't care about ordinary man.'

'My hair is natural,' shouted Mulloo. 'I've told you a thousand-thousand times.'

'I don't believe it. I just don't believe it,' shouted Janoo. 'Instead of asking who has killed all these people and why, you are blaming the victim, or at least the intended victim. Have you gone mad?'

'If you are about to blame our God-fearing religious brothers then you can stop right now,' said Tony, slamming his glass down on the table.

'Who but a religious fanatic blows himself up? For what?'

'How should I know?' shrugged Tony. 'Maybe it was someone from within her own party.'

'How can that be?' I reasoned calmly with Mulloo. 'Your mother had black hair, your father black. How come you are red?'

'I am a redhead,' screamed Mulloo. 'Get that into your thick head!'

'What nonsense, Tony!' scoffed Janoo. 'I never heard such bullshit in my life.'

'If we are so full of bullshit, ji, and also if you are going to make mean-mean-se, jealous-se comments about our hair, then I think so we'd better part companies, nahin?' said Mulloo, with a tight sa smile.

'My thoughts exactly,' said Janoo, rising to his feet. 'Come!' he barked at me, as if I was a faithful labradog sitting at his feet.

But I couldn't even argue with him in front of Mulloo, na. Bhai, izzat ka savaal tha. So I followed him out with my nose in the air. Tomorrow I'll send some flowers to her because she's having big New Year's party and my nose will be cut if I'm dropped from the invitation list. But I swear to God, she's had her hair dyed carrot. It's about as natural as Aunty Pussy's teeth.

November 2007

Musharraf declares state of emergency
Butterfly finds God

Yesterday I said to Janoo, 'Chalo, ulhumdolillah, shukrallah, thanks God, holy month of Ramzan is almost finished, mashallah. Just one more week to go and then bus, by the grace of Almighty Allah, Eid inshallah.'

Janoo raised an eyebrow and said, 'Are you also growing a beard?'

I tau clapped my hand to my chin where only yesterday I'd had my sixth laser ka dose done. Turning my back on Janoo I quickly felt with my fingers, but no stubble. Not even one or two thorn-like things poking out. And just as well, because I've already spent 18 thou rupees on it, yaar, and I've still got two sessions to go. My chin was a bit sore, but definitely no stubble. So I swung back and glared at him.

'What do you mean, beard? Beard hogi tumhari, beard ho gi tumhari maan ki, beard hogi tumhari sisters ki...'

'Metaphorically,' Janoo sighed. 'I was speaking metaphorically.'

'Stratospherically,' I replied in an equally tired si voice. 'I was speaking stratospherically.'

Just yesterday only, Kulchoo was telling me that after earth there is stratosphere and it's very, very high, higher than K-2, even. So I thought: time to show Janoo that I can also do high-high talk. Just because he's been to Oxford and is an Oxen, doesn't mean only he can use big-big words.

'Sorry?' he said, frowning at me.

'It's too late to be sorry,' I said, lifting my hairless chin proudly. 'What's been said has been said.'

'Look, I don't know what you're going on about,' he said, 'I was just making a comment, albeit a facetious one, about your new-found piety, and wondering whether you too had become a fully paid up member of the God squad. That's all!'

I think so Janoo's frightened of going to hell. He's seen me keeping all the rozas this year and saying all my namaazes. Actually he hasn't seen me too much lately, because he's been in Sharkpur where he's been interviewing teachers for his bore school, and I've been asleep in Lahore. (I go to bed after sehri, na, and don't wake till iftaari. Then I do my namaazes all in one lump sum, kazaa you know, and then I go to Mulloo Tony's for a GT or something, then I come home and watch DVDs till it's time for sehri again.) Janoo, of course, hasn't done a thing for the holy month of Ramzan. Not for a minute he's thought of praying or remembering God or anything. All month he's been sitting in his bore village in Sharkpur, where he's built a free school for children, and now he went to set up a library and fit in a computer and hire teachers and things. Imagine! And he doesn't even fight an election from there. Crack!

'It's not too late, you know,' I said. 'There's still a week to go. You can keep your rozas and Allah Almighty, the Merciful, the Beneficient, will forgive you.'

'You know something?' said Janoo, peering closely at my face, 'As you speak, I can actually see hairs sprouting from your chin...'

December 2007

Benazir Bhutto launches election campaign; Nawaz
  returns from Saudi Arabia
What's it all about? asks Butterfly

Haan, so what's new? Hmm. Nawazu is back of
course, and not in some sarha bussa PIA ka plane,
which all smell of socks and saalan, but in King
Abdullah's own gleaming golden plane, which
probably reeks of attar and serves Houbara bustard
soup and ibex pulao. And then he rode home also in
King Abdullah's apni bulletproof Merc and he
probably also called and thanked him from the
bottoms of his heart the minute he got home for
arranging everything so nicely. Not at all like last
time, haina, when he wasn't even allowed to get off
his plane? I tell you, it's always good to have friends
in high places.

Aur, Imran Khan's started eating again. He's no
longer on hunger strike. And Mush has stopped being
a general but I don't know how I'm going to recognise
him now without his vardee topi. He's handed his
stick to Kayani also so that *he* can beat us up now
instead of Mush. And Jemima has become expert on
Pakistan. So much of jalooses she's taking out and
articles she's writing in London. Shock Aziz is on his

way out—no Saudi jahaaz for him, but. And BB? Who knows what BB's up to? Pehlay tau uss ne join hands kar liye thay with Mush, na, but I think so now they've had a separation. God knows ab kiss ke saath join hands karay gee. Nawaz? The Chaudhrys? Imran? The mullahs? MQM? The republicans? Maybe she's like those Indian murtis with hundreds of hands that she can join with everyone at once without anyone knowing.

Janoo of course is shouting himself horse. 'We are not a sovereign nation!' he says. 'We're a joke! Americans are fielding their candidate, the Saudis theirs, the army is sitting on top of us, and we are getting crushed underneath.'

What else? Elections are coming. Or so Mush says. We'll believe it when we see it. Meantime, infilteration has become so much so much keh don't even ask. Servants are demanding pay rise. Dekho zara! They say they can't afford atta. So don't eat atta, baba. Eat rice. Or still better, cut out carbs altogether. Do Atkins, like me.

Uff, it was so nice and quiet when Janoo was gone. Gone where? Haw, don't you know? Janoo went to jail, baba. High point of his life and you're asking where he went? He's sooo proud of himself for being arrested with 'like-minded, responsible citizens'. Oho, he got bundled into the same van as all those Human Rights Commission Pakistani-wallahs na—the Ali Cheemas, the Meena Rehmans, the Ahmed Hossains and the Bilal Mintos of Lahore. Parha-likha, bore types. So proud he was of 'standing shoulder-to-shoulder with them'.

Pehlay tau I got a bit worried when I heard he'd been locked up. I thought maybe he's been thrown into Attock or Mianwali jail or somewhere scarey like that but when I heard he was sitting in Model Town only, with all those bore responsibles who are sure to make big fuss and get themselves out, then tau I relaxed and thought chalo, he's having nice time, and so should I. So bus, for next two days I had so much of massages and watched so many of DVDs—*Om Shanti Om*, *Desperate Housewives*, *Parineeta* again (uff, that one tau I just adore).

But then Janoo came back covered all over with mosquito bites and madder than ever. He says he's going to throw up (throw out, throw over? Whatever!) Mush now. Lo suno zara.

'Haan, Janoo,' I said, 'Zuroor. But don't you think you should make some friends in high places first?'

'Like who?' he asked.

'Hmm, let me see. How does Prince Bandar grab you?'

January 2008

Benazir Bhutto assassinated

I don't feel like going to any parties, any weddings, any GTs even. Why? Because Benazir is dead. I don't feel like going anywhere or doing anything. I don't know if I will ever feel like. I didn't like her, to be frank. She was corrupt and always doing ghuplas and pushing her own people forward. So why am I sad? So, so, so sad? I feel like someone in my family's died. I miss her.

Afterword

Let me end by telling you how *The Diary of a Social Butterfly* came to be. In the 1990s when I was working at *The Friday Times* in Lahore, my editor asked me to think of a column that would appeal to women readers. 'Touching on issues of concern to women,' he said. 'Joint family systems, working women, women's health, you get my drift? But written with a light touch. Light, but not shallow.'

So I began writing about life as a single woman in Lahore. Called 'By The Way', it documented in as light and breezy a manner as I could manage, the travails (many) and triumphs (meagre) of my own life. But after two years I got bored with it and said as much to my editor. My editor was, to use a very British phrase, 'not best pleased'. The column had grown quite popular and he was unwilling to see it perish. In the end we reached a compromise: 'By The Way' could discontinue provided I found a substitute for it.

I spent the next couple of weeks trying to find a viable alternative to 'By The Way'. But whatever I wrote morphed into a weak imitation of it. I knew if I was to write anything at all original, I had to make a radical departure from the form and style of that column. But how? With what?

Just about then I found myself at a very fancy, very big lunch party, thick with the prosperous burghers and behemoth begums of Lahore. As I was helping myself to food, I overheard a conversation between two begums.

'Haan, I bought this shahtoosh yesterday only,' a lady with rhinestone-encrusted dark glasses and diamond studs the size of rupee coins purred, as she patted the shawl in which she had swathed her ample torso. 'I had four from before also but they were shorter. So I thought, chalo, no harm in getting one in seven yards also. So I got.'

'I tau don't wear shawls, baba,' said the other, who was (almost) dressed in a micro-sleeveless blouse and a slithery, whispery, crepe sari. 'No offence, but itni thick shawl mein zara sa ayahs' wallah effect nahin aa jata?' She tossed her mane of blowdried hair over her bare shoulder and looked pityingly at her stodgy lunch companion.

That was my Eureka moment. I knew then that I should do a satirical column based on the lives of the rich and inane. But how was I to do it without naming names and making enemies? I needed a fictitious character who would not only be my mouthpiece, but also personify all the neuroses and insecurities to which people in her position are prey. Enter the Butterfly. But in order to make her silliness apparent, I needed a counterpoint. Hence, Janoo. Janoo would need a family—The Old Bag, the Gruesome twosome; and so would the Butterfly—Mummy, Aunty Pussy, Jonkers. They would have one child, Kulchoo, and live in Lahore. Janoo would be landed and educated, the Butterfly urban and foolish, and their marriage

224

would be built on mutual misunderstanding. I had my column. Or at least the idea for it.

When I discussed it with my editor, he was lukewarm but allowed me, albeit grudgingly, to have a go. The column was an immediate hit with my readers. It was new and yet familiar. It held a mirror up to them but was sufficiently good-humoured to cause no—or very little—offence. What's more, after two or three issues, it even won my editor over.

In the many years that I have been writing *The Diary of a Social Butterfly*, the question that I am asked most often about it is this: by whom is the central character inspired? I consider the query a compliment. For it means that my protagonist, the shallow, egotistical, obtuse Butterfly, is sufficiently credible for my readers to feel that she is based on a real person of my acquaintance. Though I often respond to the query with vague denials, the fact is that the Butterfly *is* based on someone I know intimately: myself.

The Butterfly is the embodiment of my own 'hidden shallows'. I may not speak or live like her. I may not even have the same taste in music and film. Nonetheless, the Butterfly is a true expression of my *Hello*-reading, self-absorbed, frivolous side, exaggerated manifold and unredeemed by any hint of self-doubt and unburdened by any desire for a more meaningful existence. Of course, I cannot claim to be the inspiration for each and every one of her concerns and quests. I simply wouldn't have thought of them. So, I borrow shamelessly from other people. When I hear of a particularly comic incident, I promptly cull it for the column. Many of the incidents described in this collection, such as the burglary where the burglars lectured their hapless victims on their unseemly dress, have really happened, not to me but to others. Many of the conversations relayed here, I have overheard. And in reporting some of the scandals written up in the diary, I have crossed over from fiction to fact.

True to my original brief to address real-life issues, I have attempted to confront the concerns that govern the daily life of a character such as the Butterfly. Hence her preoccupation with in-laws, kala jadoo, mannats and money; holidays abroad, shopping, designerwear and money; domestic staff, BMWs, botox and money; society weddings, charity balls, scandals and money; property, Bollywood, divorce and money. I have also tried to include in this column the bigger events of our times that have reverberated even in the life of one as coddled as the Butterfly. So 9/11, the invasion of Iraq, the Kashmir earthquake, the tsunami, Lal Masjid and Benazir's assassination, as they have impacted the Butterfly, have all been recorded in this diary. Moreover, the larger socio-political trends of recent years have also, I hope, been adequately reflected in the Butterfly's life: the face-off between civil society and the army, the rise of consumerism, the increasing cultural alienation of the rich, the gradual breakdown of law and order, the media revolution, women's growing presence in the workplace, the tension between landed gentry and new money, and the multifarious pleasures and pains of globalisation. So without ever intending to be, *The Diary of a Social Butterfly* has become a record—compiled admittedly by a rather cross-eyed observer—of some of Pakistan's most turbulent years.

That is not to say that I have ever approached it as a sociological treatise. With a protagonist as frivolous as the Butterfly, there was only so much seriousness that this column could reasonably accommodate. For me it has been, and continues to be, great fun to write. More than thinking up themes or creating situations and introducing characters, I have enjoyed inventing the language that has become the Butterfly's sine qua non. And in this effort Lahoris of my acquaintance have—often unknowingly—helped hugely. On my own, I would never have been able to think up priceless phrases like 'three-tiara cake', 'paindu pastry', 'do number ka maal' and, my personal favourite, 'what cheeks!' Nor would I have had the imagination to 'slip into a comma', to meet 'business typhoons and textile magnets' or 'get knocked up by a truck'. And I certainly would not have 'laughed till I became historical'. For this unintended largesse I thank my Pakistani friends, relatives and acquaintances.

I owe another enormous thank you to my sister, Jugnu Mohsin, who, for the last twelve years that I have been living in London, cut off for the main part from the comings and goings of Lahori society, has fed me the priceless gems and nuggets that have allowed this column to continue. Without her encouragement and input, it would have died long since. To my original editor, Najam Sethi, my deep gratitude for giving me the space and indulgence to begin this diary on the pages of his esteemed newspaper. Were it not for his persistent haranguing, it would never have been compiled into a book either. My thanks also to Chiki Sarkar, my effervescent editor, who helped me realise the full potential of the Butterfly.

A note on the author

Moni Mohsin is the author of *Tender Hooks* and *The End of Innocence*. She writes a popular column called 'The Diary of a Social Butterfly' for Pakistan's *Friday Times*, selections of which make up this, her second book. She grew up in Lahore and now divides her time between Lahore and London, where she lives with her husband and two children.